Computer Applications for Life Sciences

Revised Edition

Joan M. Harnett, OP, PhD.

Departments of Mathematics and Computer Science
Manhattan College
Riverdale, New York

LINUS Learning

Published by Linus Learning.

Ronkonkoma, NY 11779

ISBN 10: 1-60797-501-7

ISBN 13: 978-1-60797-501-4

Printed in the United States of America.

This book is printed on acid-free paper.

Print Number 5 4 3 2 1

Table of Contents

Acknowledgment

This work was completed while on sabbatical leave from Manhattan College.

Introduction

The curricula for Life Science programs include a variety of Mathematics courses ranging from Linear Analysis to Calculus. In those courses various theories and applications pertaining to Biology, Radiology, Allied Health and Exercise Science are presented and studied.

In this text we will explore the use of those mathematical concepts in a very intuitive way to study data – and ways to manipulate it – to help us create a picture and understanding of the mathematics that underlie issues in the health sciences. Consider questions such as: How effective is a drug treatment? How are the cells of a virus increasing or decreasing? Did the exercise program we recently initiated really have any impact on the participants?

We will use a variety of computer applications to do the heavy work of the number crunching so that we can concentrate our time and energy on the creation of appropriate models and on gaining insights into what the data may tell us.

The text is divided into seven chapters. We will consider the mechanics of the particular computer programs we use as a tool, starting with Microsoft Excel®. Other Spreadsheet software such as Apache OpenOffice™ will be mentioned, but typically the basic structure and functionality of OpenOffice closely follows that of Excel. A rule of thumb is to use the help feature of OpenOffice to find the corresponding form for the command presented in Excel.

In the second and third chapters, we use Excel to create pictures of data and see how to use those pictures to help create mathematical models for the data – a simple way to capture the relationships between two aspects of a scenario, such as the relationship between time spent practicing free throws and the number of points a basketball player actually achieves in a given season.

Chapters 4 through 6 use both Excel and the statistical software program IBM SPSS Statistics 19 to calculate statistics that help us summarize the data we've collected in various studies, and to draw reliable conclusions about what the data might be indicating. We will also see how known patterns of numbers, called probability distributions, can help us understand the likelihood of certain events occurring.

Lastly, Chapter 7 presents the mechanics for manipulating matrices using a spreadsheet. This can be a valuable tool in a variety of mathematical applications.

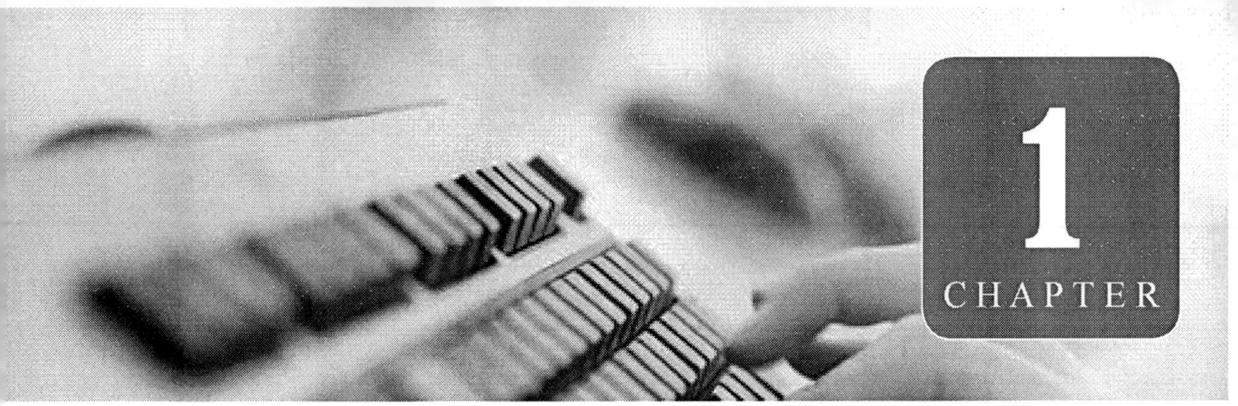

Using Spreadsheets for Research

WORKSHEET BASICS

This text will present various research and modeling techniques, primarily using Excel 2010 in the Windows® operating system, but the basic concepts extend to most spreadsheets. This is not a text about Excel per say. If you have not used Excel before you might want to invest some time using one of the many tutorials available online, but we will highlight some basic terminology to begin.

The Excel file is called a **workbook**, illustrated in the screen below. Each workbook consists of 3 spreadsheets to start, accessed via the tabs at the bottom labeled **Sheet1**, **Sheet2**, and **Sheet3.** Additional spreadsheets (pages) can be added or deleted. The tabs can (and should) be renamed to reflect the information on the sheet. To rename the sheet, double click on the tab. You will see the current name in white on black print, Sheet1 Simply type in the new name. The spreadsheet is divided into a grid of numbered rows and columns designated by letters. The box which is the intersection of each row and column is called a cell and is labeled by the column letter and row number of its location. The highlighted box below is cell A1.

The cell is the primary unit of the spreadsheet. It can contain text such as a label, a number or a formula.

Starting with the 2007 version, Microsoft reorganized the many built-in functions of MS Office by replacing the menu bar containing the terms File, Edit and so on with tabs at the top of the page. Each tab has a wide band called the **ribbon** and each ribbon is divided into **groups**. Take a moment to browse through the various tabs noting the change in ribbons and various group names. The titles of the groups written along the bottom of the ribbon can sometimes be easy to miss because they are written in a pale font. Two symbols that are particularly useful are ? **help** at the upper right corner of the screen and the **undo arrow** on the top left side of the screen.

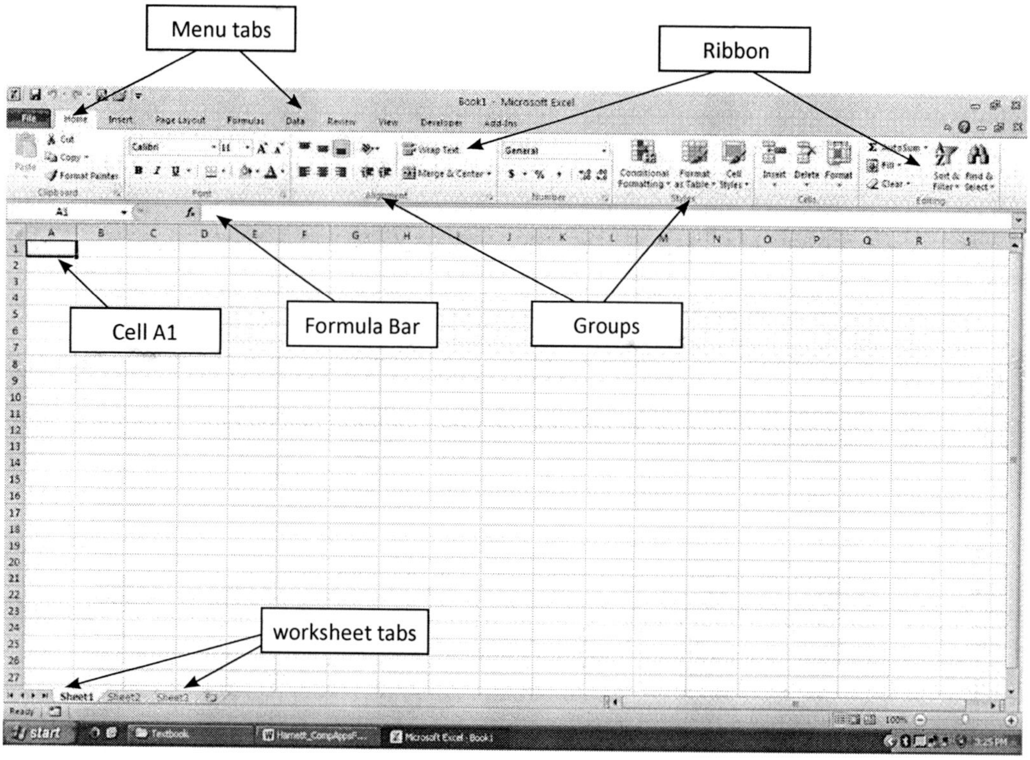

Figure 1.1

Cells may be formatted for size, color, borders, fill color and so on. There are predefined formats available (Home ribbon/Styles Group/ Cell Styles Menu) or you can create your own. Allow yourself some time to investigate the various possibilities and see what you like. As a rule of thumb, be careful to choose a format that highlights your data, especially parameters and results. There is a temptation to make the spreadsheet very showy simply because you can. However, you don't want the spreadsheet to be so busy that the basic information is camouflaged in the process.

Some particularly useful formatting tools are found on the Home ribbon / Alignment Group. Wrapping Text allows you to maintain a balanced column width when the titles of the columns are long. Merge and Center creates a centered heading over the active columns of the spreadsheet. Illustrations of the two formats are shown below in figure 1.2a and b.

In figure 1.2a (Electoral College Votes, Population, and Area by State, http://mathforum.org/workshops/sum96/data.collections/datalibrary/ElectoralPopArea.xls) note that the entire heading "Electoral College Votes and Area by State" is contained in cell A1. In order to spread the title across columns A to F, select those columns in row 1 (left click and drag). Click on the "Merge and Center" option in the Alignment group. To adjust the heading "Electoral Votes" in column B, select cell B3 and click on the "Wrap Text" option in the Alignment group. If at any point a cell contains the entry ######, that's a clue that the cell is not wide enough to display the information stored there. Make the column wider to properly display the information.

We will revisit this data in the next chapter.

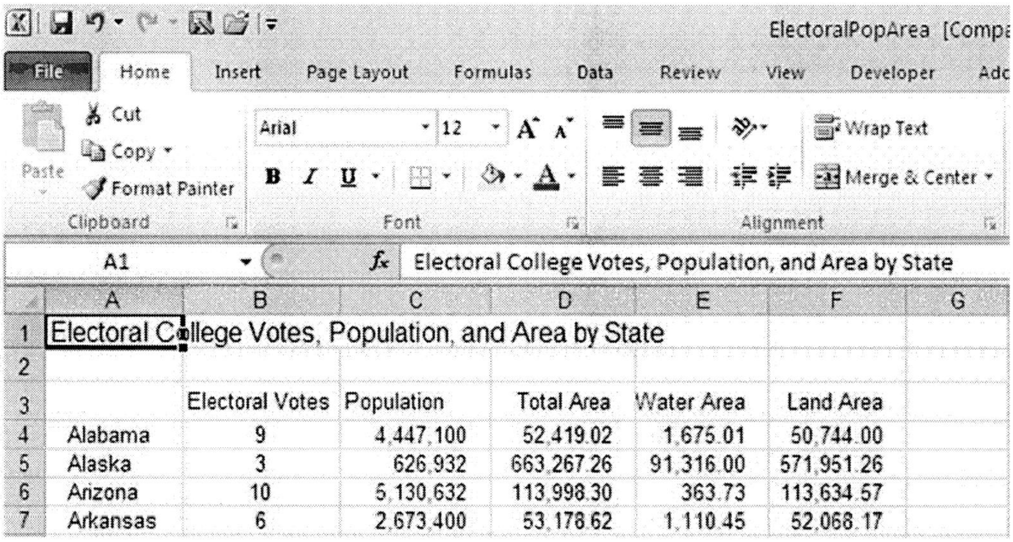

Figure 1.2a

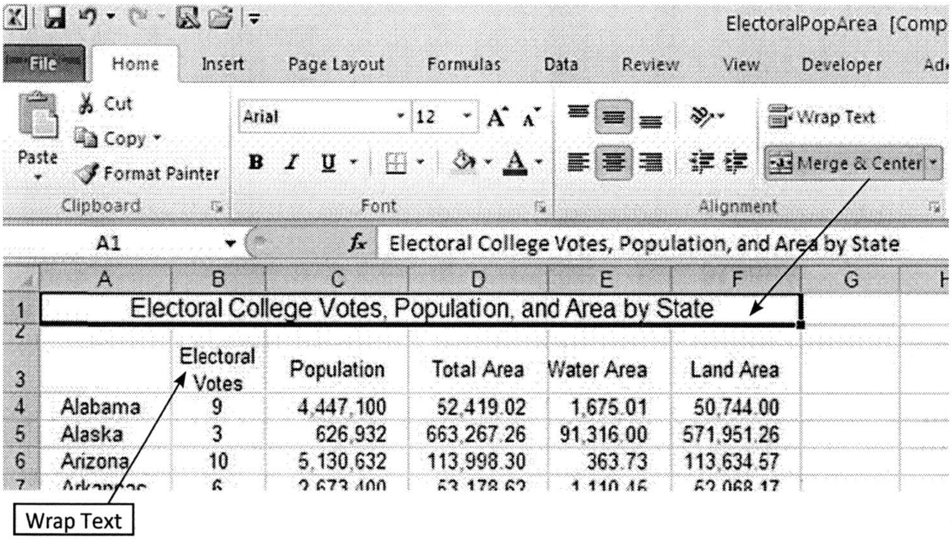

Figure 1.2 b

Cursor Shapes

It is important to pay attention to the shape the cursor takes as you perform various tasks in the spreadsheet. You sometimes may need to move the mouse a bit until the desired shape is visible. Below is a summary of what to look for.

Shape	Function
	This is the basic cursor; shows location in the spreadsheet.
	Cross hairs: Click and drag to move the contents of the cell to a new location.
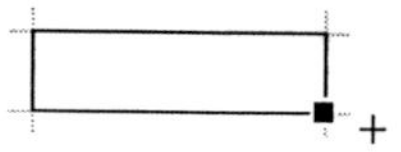	Plus symbol when hovering over the small square on the bottom right corner of a cell: Click and drag to replicate a formula or copy the contents of a cell.

Table 1.1

Formulas and Functions

Excel provides numerous built-in formulas and functions commonly used in mathematics and business. To see the complete list click on the function symbol f_x at the formula bar just above the column labels (see figure 1.1). I will highlight a few formulas here that are generally helpful. Others will be introduced in other chapters as needed.

We will use the following table to illustrate some common formulas

	A	B	C	D
1				TOTAL
2	1	2	3	
3	6	5	4	
4	11	8	5	
5	16	11	6	

Table 1.2

In general the pattern of entering formulas follows these basic steps:

First, in order to signal the use of a formula, **start by typing the = symbol.**

Second, you want to use the CELL NAME rather than the value stored in the cell. This way if a particular number changes, the results will be automatically updated since the formula uses whatever value is currently sitting in the cell.

Third, you may enter your own formula or one of the built-in ones.

For example to add the contents of the cells in row 2, you can type = A2 + B2 + C2 in cell D2. You can also use the built in function SUM( ) entered in cell D2 as = SUM(A2:C2).

Most of the built-in formulas allow you to specify a range of cells by means of a "Click and Drag" movement, that is point to the starting cell (A2), click the left mouse button, hold the button down and slide to the last cell in the range (C2). You can also type the phrase A2:C2 directly. You can specify non-contiguous cells by means of a comma: =SUM(A2, A4, B4, C5) is equivalent to = A2 + A4 + B4 + C5.

Formula Replication

Once a formula has been entered, you can copy it down the column by selecting cell D2. Note that the bottom border contains a small square at the right corner. As you move the mouse over that square, the cursor will change to + (Table 1.1). Click on the square and drag down to find the totals for the remaining rows. Notice that the cell names will be changed automatically to reflect the change in row. You may have to practice this action since even a slight movement away from the square will result in the loss of the "+" cursor.

Other functions that are set up in much the same way are =AVERAGE(A2:C2), =MAX(A2:C2) and =MIN(A2:C2).

	A	B	C	D	E	F	G
1				TOTAL	AVERAGE	MAXIMUM	MINIMUM
2	1	2	3	6	2	3	1
3	6	5	4	15	5	6	4
4	11	8	5	24	8	11	5
5	16	11	6	33	11	16	6

Table 1.3 a

	A	B	C	D	E	F	G
1				TOTAL	AVERAGE	MAXIMUM	MINIMUM
2	1	2	3	=SUM(A2:C2)	=AVERAGE(A2:C2)	=MAX(A2:C2)	=MIN(A2:C2)
3	6	5	4	=SUM(A3:C3)	=AVERAGE(A3:C3)	=MAX(A3:C3)	=MIN(A3:C3)
4	11	8	5	=SUM(A4:C4)	=AVERAGE(A4:C4)	=MAX(A4:C4)	=MIN(A4:C4)
5	16	11	6	=SUM(A5:C5)	=AVERAGE(A5:C5)	=MAX(A5:C5)	=MIN(A5:C5)

Table 1.3 b

Of course these formulas apply to columns as well as rows. The total for column A, for example is = SUM(A2:A5). Similarly, the sum of all numbers in the first three columns would be =SUM(A2:C5).

Another formula with this format is = COUNT(A2:A5). This counts the number of cells in the range that contain numbers only, in this case 12. A slight variation COUNTA( ) will return the number of non-empty cells regardless of what they contain.

Absolute Reference

In the replication of formulas above, it was noted that the formulas were automatically adjusted **relative** to the row to which they were copied. However, there are times when the same value should be used in every formula in the column and should not change regardless of the row or column. For example, if you are converting temperatures from the Celsius scale to Fahrenheit, the conversion factor is the same for all data: F= 9/5 C + 32. If we place the constants 9/5 and 32 in cells B1 and B2, respectively, every Fahrenheit formula should use those cells in the conversion calculation. We want cells B1 and B2 to be **absolute references,** that is, non-changing. The designation for an absolute reference is the $ symbol. It is applied separately to both the column reference and the row reference in the cell's name. So we will use $B$1 to represent 9/5 and $B$2 to represent 32. The conversion formula is a linear equation so we label 9/5 "slope" and 32 "intercept". Notice that the references to column A values are relative – they change according to the row, but the references to both the slope and intercept are absolute – every calculation uses the same values. Once you have typed a cell location in a formula you can take a shortcut to inserting the absolute reference $'s by highlighting the cell name (B1, for example) and pressing function key F4. The cell reference will become $B$1.

	A	B
1	slope	1.8
2	intercept	32
3		
4	Celcius	Fahrenheit
5	-20	-4
6	-10	14
7	0	32
8	10	50
9	20	68
10	30	86
11	40	104
12	50	122
13	60	140
14	70	158
15	80	176
16	90	194
17	100	212

Table 1.4 a

	A	B
1	slope	=9/5
2	intercept	32
3		
4	Celcius	Fahrenheit
5	-20	=$B$1*A5+$B$2
6	-10	=$B$1*A6+$B$2
7	0	=$B$1*A7+$B$2
8	10	=$B$1*A8+$B$2
9	20	=$B$1*A9+$B$2
10	30	=$B$1*A10+$B$2
11	40	=$B$1*A11+$B$2
12	50	=$B$1*A12+$B$2
13	60	=$B$1*A13+$B$2
14	70	=$B$1*A14+$B$2
15	80	=$B$1*A15+$B$2
16	90	=$B$1*A16+$B$2
17	100	=$B$1*A17+$B$2

Table 1.4 b

It is also possible to designate a column only or a row only as absolute. You would just use one $ symbol in front of either the column part of the cell name or the row part, such as $B1 or B$1.

More Numerical Functions

Three additional functions to place in your collection of tools include

- = ROUND(*value, number of decimal places*) rounds a real number off to the desired number of decimal places.
- = RAND( ) generates random decimal values between 0 and 1. Random number generators are the basis of many games as well as simulations of experiments.
- = RANDBETWEEN(*min value, maxvalue*) generates random integers between the two numbers given. For example, one might use = RANDBETWEEN(1, 6) to simulate the roll of a die.

Conditional Formulas

There are a variety of formulas that are executed IF some stated condition is met. A sampling of these functions includes IF( ), COUNTIF( ) and AVERAGEIF( ). In each of the following commands, **comparison** refers to a phrase using some form of <, >, = evaluations. This phrase is also called the criterion.

For the COUNTIF( ) and AVERAGEIF( ) commands, the criterion is entered as a string starting with the symbol such as ">10". The **range** refers to the cell names to include in the search for qualifying values written in the same form as the formulas above, first_cell:last_cell which can be defined by the click and drag method.

Formula	Purpose
=IF(comparison, true result, false result)	Two possible outcomes: if the comparison is true give the first result, otherwise give the second result
= COUNTIF(range, comparison)	Count how many values meet the criterion.
= AVERAGEIF(range, comparison)	Include numbers in the average if they meet the criterion. Note there is a third parameter that is optional. I recommend that it be left off.

Table 1.5

Here is an illustration of the conditional formulas listed in Table 1.5. The following is a gradebook for a class that has had 3 exams. The IF command is used to determine whether or not a comment is made. The empty string "" represents *nothing*, that is, leave the cell blank. COUNTIF is used to tell the number of passing and failing grades, and AVERAGEIF is used to give the average of passing grades and the average of failing grades.

	A	B	C	D	E
1	EXAM1	EXAM	EXAM 3	AVERAGE	Comment
2	81	47	78	=AVERAGE(A2:C2)	=IF(D2<60,"Fail","")
3	93	100	81	=AVERAGE(A3:C3)	=IF(D3<60,"Fail","")
4	100	88	83	=AVERAGE(A4:C4)	=IF(D4<60,"Fail","")
5	52	73	75	=AVERAGE(A5:C5)	=IF(D5<60,"Fail","")
6	35	75	57	=AVERAGE(A6:C6)	=IF(D6<60,"Fail","")
7	100	87	100	=AVERAGE(A7:C7)	=IF(D7<60,"Fail","")
8	84	61	39	=AVERAGE(A8:C8)	=IF(D8<60,"Fail","")
9	13	62	65	=AVERAGE(A9:C9)	=IF(D9<60,"Fail","")
10	22	66	68	=AVERAGE(A10:C10)	=IF(D10<60,"Fail","")
11					
12	Number Passed:		=COUNTIF(D2:D10,">=60")	Average P:	=AVERAGEIF(D2:D10,">=60")
13	Number Failed:		=COUNTIF(D2:D10,"<60")	Average F:	=AVERAGEIF(D2:D10,"<60")

Table 1.6 a

	A	B	C	D	E
1	EXAM 1	EXAM 2	EXAM 3	AVERAGE	Comment
2	81	47	78	68.7	
3	93	100	81	91.3	
4	100	88	83	90.3	
5	52	73	75	66.7	
6	35	75	57	55.7	Fail
7	100	87	100	95.7	
8	84	61	39	61.3	
9	13	62	65	46.7	Fail
10	22	66	68	52.0	Fail
11					
12	Number Passed:		6	Average P:	79.0
13	Number Failed:		3	Average F:	51.4

Table 1.6 b

The above gradebook uses the conditional functions in their simplest forms, but these functions may have significant complexity. The IF command may contain several layers of options which will be illustrated in the next section. COUNTIF and AVERAGEIF have multi-criteria counterparts (COUNTIFS and AVERAGEIFS) which are left to the reader to explore.

VLOOKUP Table

Suppose we want to insert a new column GRADES between the AVERAGE and Comment columns in Table 1.6. We'd like the program to assign a letter grade that corresponds to the average. We can achieve this by using a "nested" IF statement to define all possible grades. The entry for the new GRADE column E for the first set of marks would be

=IF(D2>=90,"A", IF(D2>=80,"B", IF(D2>=70,"C", IF(D2>=60, "D","F"))))

Note that each IF statement is completely contained in the *False Result* section on the previous IF statement – look at the parentheses. You can think of this as peeling off layers of possibilities. "Is this average an A? No, well then, is it a B?" and so on until the last IF which says "Is this average a D? No, then it must be an F!" If the answer to the comparison is yes at any point the function ends and returns the letter associated with the *True Result* clause.

Another way to assign the grades is by means of a look-up table. We begin by creating a chart that has a standard set of values. For the gradebook above we have the values shown in Figure 1.3. The first column of the chart contains the lowest (or threshold) value that determines the grade. This column must be sorted in ascending order. There can be any number of additional columns that are part of our information chart. We have added Quality Points as well as letter grades.

The general form of the command

= VLOOKUP(lookup value, table range, col index num, [interval threshold or exact value])

- **lookup value** refers to an actual value or the cell name where the value is located –in our example, the average that needs to be found in the look-up table.
- **Table range** is the location of the table; upper left cell: bottom right cell of the data part of the chart. Do not include headings. Use absolute references so all values are looking at the same table.
- **col index num** refers to the column number of the item returned. Grades are in column 2 and quality points are in column 3.
- **interval_threshold or exact_value** is an optional TRUE/FALSE entry. The default is interval (TRUE), that is, all numbers starting at the threshold value up to but not including the next threshold number. An F in our chart will be assigned to all values from 0 up to 59.9. If we use the exact value option (FALSE), only exact matches will receive a value from the chart. All other values will generate the message #N/A, an error message that says the value is Not Available. We might use the FALSE option if our chart gave only letters and quality points. We would need an exact value of "B" to receive 2.0 as the quality points value.

	A	B	C	D	E	F	G
1	EXAM 1	EXAM 2	EXAM 3	AVERAGE	GRADE	QPts	Comment
2	81	47	78	68.7	D	1.0	
3	93	100	81	91.3	A	4.0	
4	100	88	83	90.3	A	4.0	
5	71	73	75	73.0	C	2.0	
6	35	75	57	55.7	F	0.0	Fail
7	100	87	79	88.7	B	3.0	
8	84	61	65	70.0	C	2.0	
9	13	62	65	46.7	F	0.0	Fail
10	22	66	68	52.0	F	0.0	Fail
11							
12	Number Passed: 6			Average:		80.3	
13	Number Failed: 3			Average:		51.4	
14							
15				Grading Policy			
16				Average	Grade	Quality Points	
17				0	F	0.0	
18				60	D	1.0	
19				70	C	2.0	
20				80	B	3.0	
21				90	A	4.0	
22							

Figure 1.3

The VLOOKUP command is now entered into column E (GRADE) and column F (QPts). The first entry for each column is

=VLOOKUP(D2,$D$17:$E$21,**2**) and =VLOOKUP(D2,$D$17:$E$21,**3**), respectively.

E	F
GRADE	QPts
=VLOOKUP(D2,$D$17:$F$21,2)	=VLOOKUP(D2,$D$17:$F$21,3)
=VLOOKUP(D3,$D$17:$F$21,2)	=VLOOKUP(D3,$D$17:$F$21,3)
=VLOOKUP(D4,$D$17:$F$21,2)	=VLOOKUP(D4,$D$17:$F$21,3)
=VLOOKUP(D5,$D$17:$F$21,2)	=VLOOKUP(D5,$D$17:$F$21,3)

Figure 1.4

The "**V**" of VLOOKUP stands for vertical meaning that the chart is arranged in columns. There is also a horizontal HLOOKUP if you prefer to work with rows.

Designing Reports

While Excel will create impressive spreadsheets and results, most studies will require a written report, typically composed in Word or possibly a scientific word processor. It is often most effective to "show" portions of a table or pictures of the data that have been created in the spreadsheet. Most elements in Excel can be copied and pasted into Word. Occasionally when importing from other applications it is necessary to "Paste Special". Be aware that such imports can be linked to the source documents. Every time a change is made to the source, the copy in the Word document changes as well. While there may be times when this link is beneficial, more often you'll want a "snapshot" of the spreadsheet showing a particular result at a particular time.

If you are presenting your results in the spreadsheet itself, it is advisable to format it in a way that is visually pleasing. Use cell fills and borders to highlight starting values and assumptions. Cells can be formatted in a conditional manner (Home tab/Styles group/ Conditional Formatting option). For example, using the data in figure 1.3 we can have failing grades display in red. Choose New Rule and stipulate "Format only cells that contain" and fill in the dropdown options as shown.

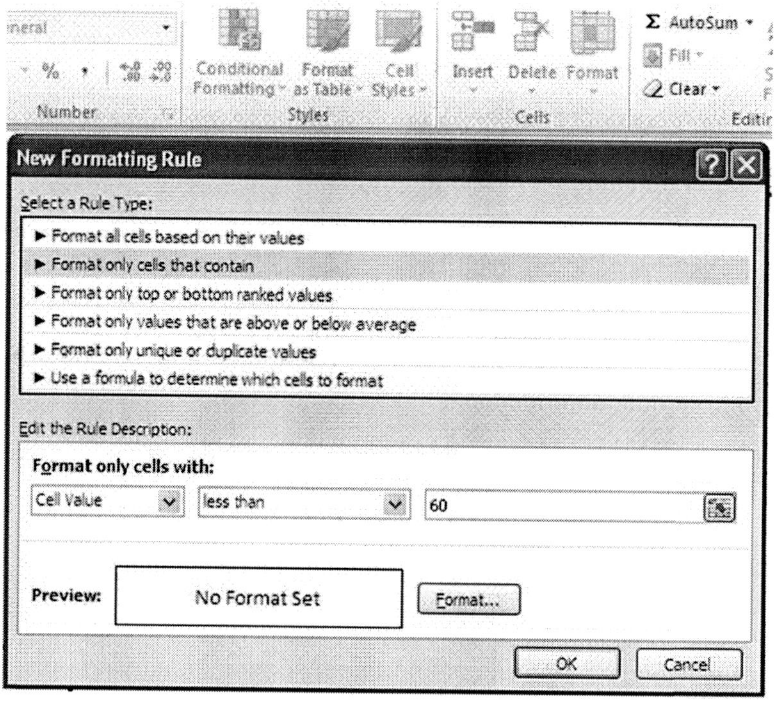

Figure 1.5

Now click on Format... to change the color of these cells

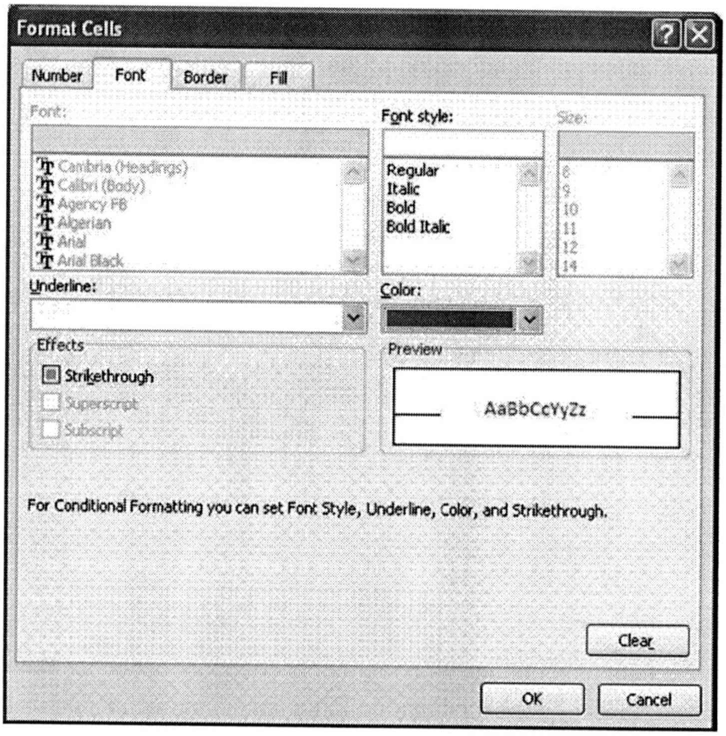

Figure 1.6

Press OK to close each dialog box. Make sure to show the rules for This Worksheet and Apply.

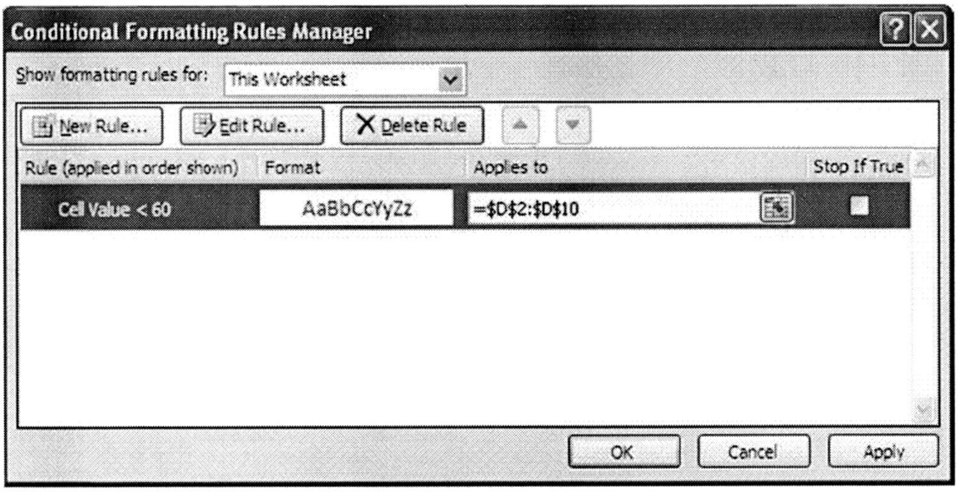

Figure 1.7

All the averages in column D that are below 60 will now turn red.

When printing the spreadsheet (File/Print), be sure to check the preview to make sure that your data fits the page as desired. Spreadsheets are often printed in Landscape (see Page Layout) orientation to accommodate a larger number of columns.

EXERCISES

Create a spreadsheet for the Height and Weight data given below:

- Use word wrap for headings
- Use borders and fills to create good visual effects.
- Place the title (BMI Calculations) in merged cells centered across the top of the table.
- Rename the tab at the bottom of the sheet as BMI.
- Enter the formula for BMI, using 1 decimal place accuracy for the results.

$$\text{BMI} = \frac{\text{mass}(\text{lb})}{(\text{height}(\text{in}))^2} \times 703$$

- Use the following information from the National Heart Lung and Blood Institute (http://www.nhlbi.nih.gov/guidelines/obesity/BMI/bmicalc.htm) to create a VLOOKUP table:

  BMI Categories:

  - o Underweight <18.5
  - o Normal weight = 18.5–24.9

  - o Overweight = 25–29.9
  - o Obesity = BMI of 30 or greater
- Include totals for each category using COUNTIF.

	Weight	Height			
StuID	pounds (lbs)	Feet	Inches	BMI	Category
10010	102	4	10	21.3	Normal
10020	135	5	4	23.2	Normal
10030	285	6	1	37.6	Obese
10040	194	6	0	...	...
10050	206	6	0	...	...
10060	190	6	2	...	...
10070	275	5	11	...	...
10080	175	5	5	...	...
10090	140	6	5	...	...
10100	150	5	2	...	...
10110	190	5	9	...	...
10120	120	5	5	...	...
10130	185	5	8	...	...
10140	190	5	5	...	...
10150	165	5	11	...	...
10160	205	6	4	...	...
Totals:	Under	Normal	Over	Obese	

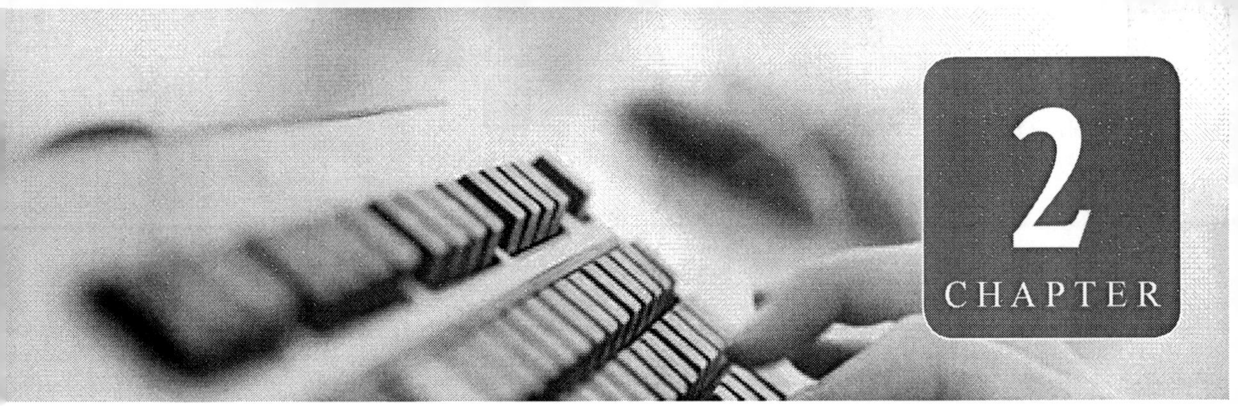

Visualizing Data

One of the great things about using electronic spreadsheets is the ability to create quick, reliable "snapshots" that give us a more intuitive understanding of the data we have collected.

A good first step in modeling and analyzing data is to get an idea of what it looks like. Suppose you have collected data about a particular experiment or activity. You may suspect that there is a connection between two of the characteristics or facets that you have observed. So let's get a picture of what, if anything, is going on between these two quantities.

We'll create a scatter plot, a graph that is simply a collection of points, one point for each pair of numbers in the data set. For example below are 2 scatter plots representing data from the spreadsheet Electoral College Votes, Population, and Area by State. (http://mathforum.org/workshops/sum96/data.collections/datalibrary/ElectoralPopArea.xls)

The first diagram represents the total area in square miles and the population for each state in the United States. There is no particular pattern to the points and so we could conclude that there is no significant relationship between a state's physical size and the number of electoral votes that it casts. Even so, it is interesting to take a closer look at the 3 points that are removed from the main cluster (circled on the graph). These are referred to as "outliers" since they are clearly removed from the general location of all the other data points. As marked on the graph, the 3 points represent Alaska, Texas and California. Outliers sometimes highlight an error in data entry or, as is the case here, represent true exceptions to the general case.

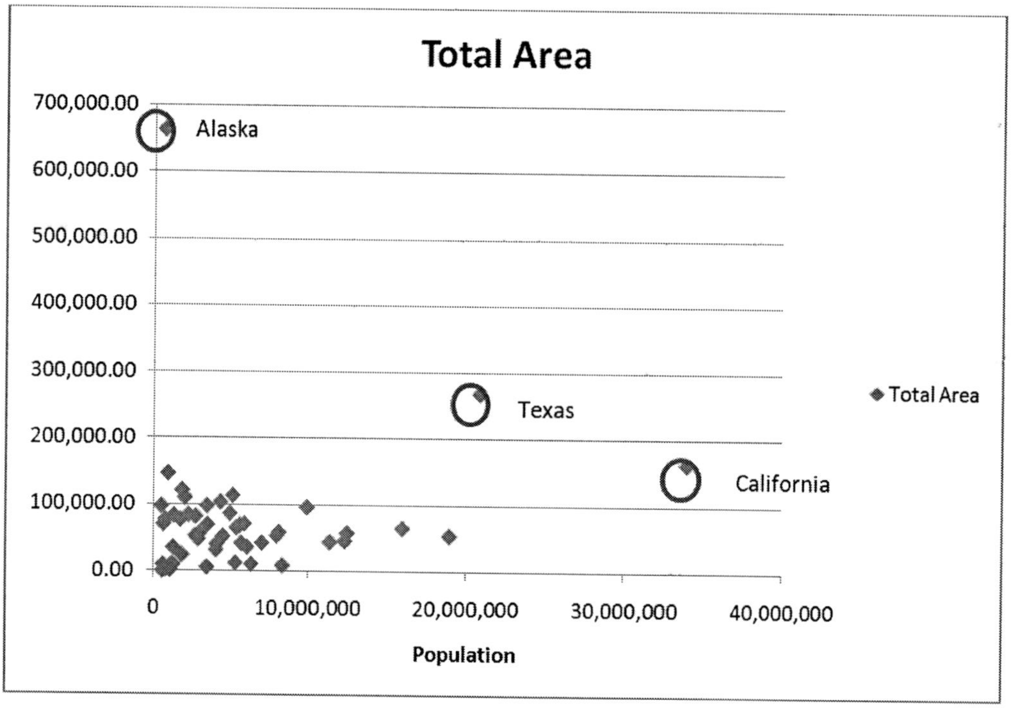

Figure 2.1

If we now consider the same spreadsheet and plot population and number of electoral votes we see a very clear linear relationship: the more people residing in the state, the more electoral votes that state has.

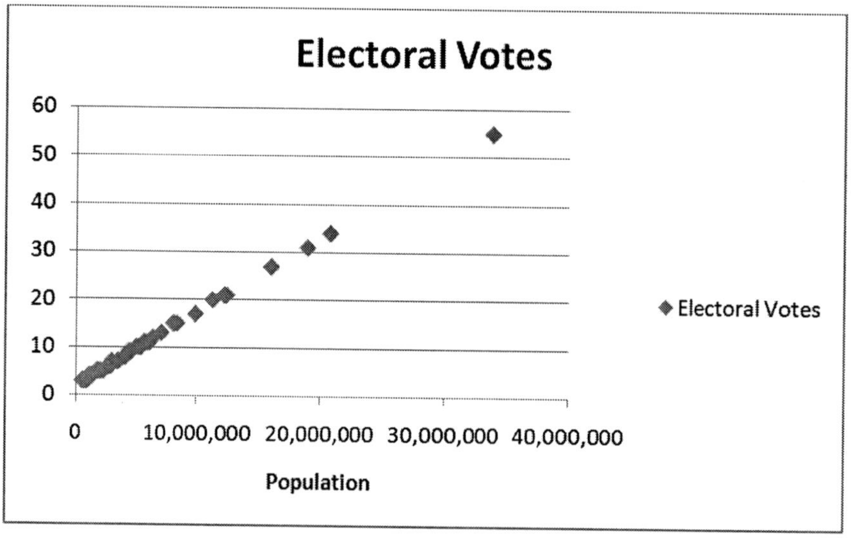

Figure 2.2

So let's explore some data and see if a pattern exists and how we can describe that pattern mathematically.

The following data, a set of measures of the width (W) and length (L) of the shells of 88 butter clams found along the shore of Puget Sound in west Seattle, may be downloaded. (The Quantitative Environmental Learning Project (QELP), Greg Langkamp and Joe Hull, Seattle Central Community College, http://www.seattlecentral.edu/qelp/sets/001/001.html) Verify that you have 88 pairs of measurements (try using COUNT()!)

The data should be entered in two continuous columns (one for W and one for L). To plot the scatter diagram:

1. Click on the Insert tab of the menu bar at the top of the window
2. Select all data and titles for the **W** and **L** columns (click and drag). The two columns should be completely highlighted (all 88 data points.)
3. On the Charts Group of the Ribbon:
    a. Choose Scatter
    b. Choose Scatter with only Markers

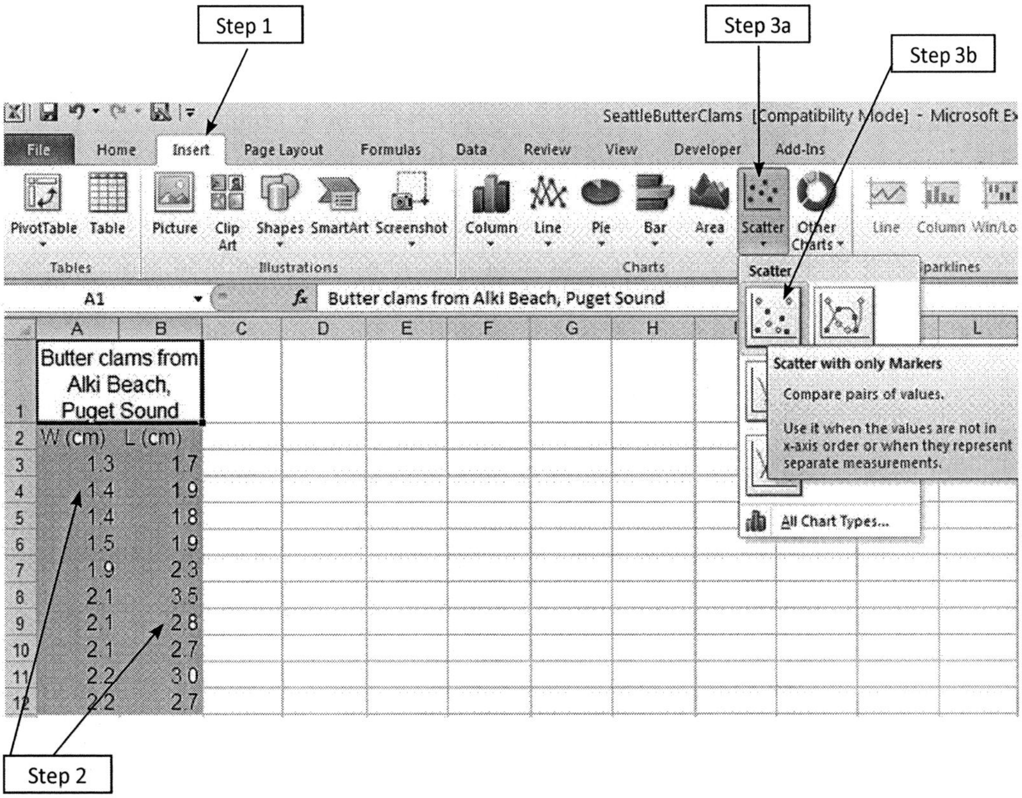

Figure 2.3

The following graph will appear:

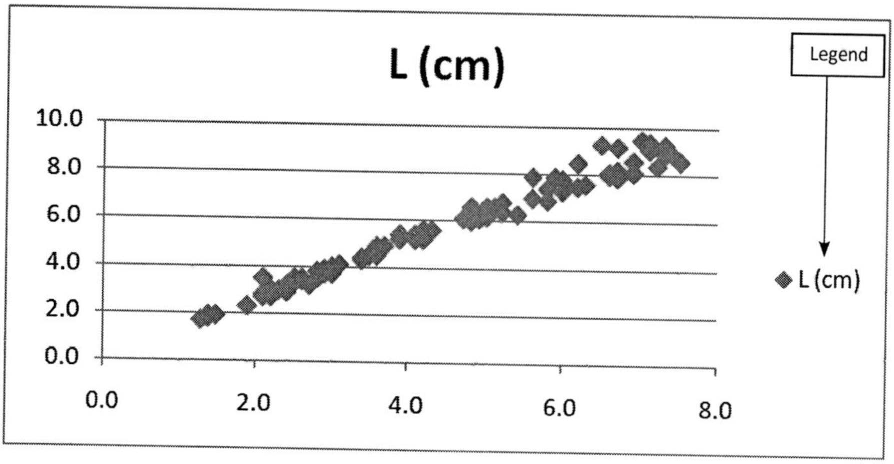

Figure 2.4

There are several text boxes that can be added to (or deleted from) the graph to make it more informative. The area on the far right is called the legend. It is helpful to show which symbol represents a particular data set (or series) when a graph contains more than one data series.

There are also a variety of labels that can be used including the chart title, and titles for the primary horizontal (width) and vertical (length) axes. These options are made available by first selecting the graph, that is, while pointing to the graph use a single left click. A set of Chart Tools will appear on the ribbon. In the Labels section choose the options for Chart Title and then for Axis Titles. Since our graph contains only 1 set of data, let's delete the legend on the right hand side, by selecting it and pressing the delete button on the keyboard. The chart should now look something like:

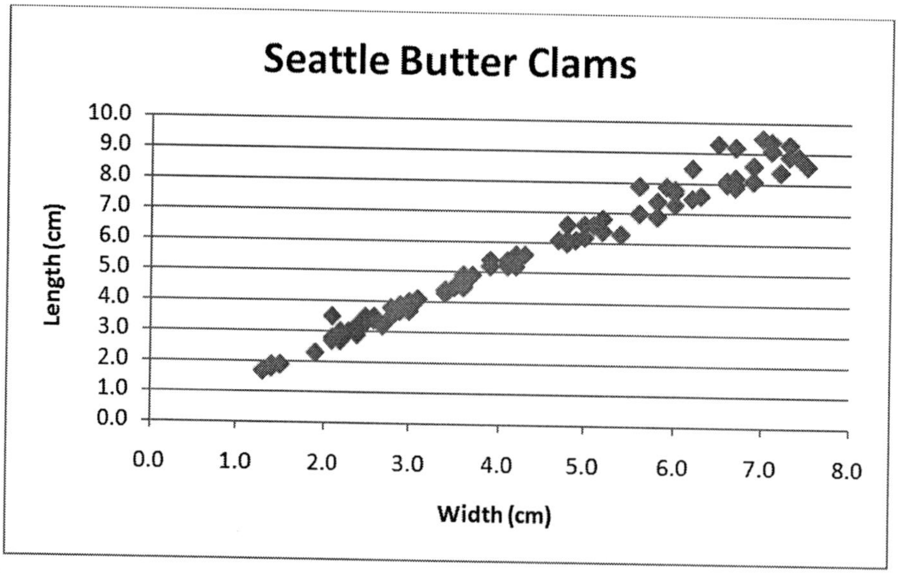

Figure 2.5

EXERCISES

1. In a study to determine plant cover in a desert area, plots were created and the diameter of each plant within the plot was measured. The following table shows the x and y coordinates for each plant in one such plot (used with permission, Dr. Lance Evans, Biology Department, Manhattan College, Riverdale, NY).

   Create the scatter plot which in this case acts as a roadmap marking the location of each plant.

Plant	x-dist	y-dist	Plant	x-dist	y-dist
P1	0.1	1.6	P23	9.55	16.25
P2	0.9	1.1	P24	7.45	15.8
P3	1.85	2.2	P25	7.35	16.2
P4	1.4	4.6	P26	6.85	14.85
P5	0.4	5.35	P27	1.35	18.7
P6	3.35	4.4	P28	1.65	23.4
P7	4.35	2.9	P29	5.85	15.6
P8	5.3	2	P30	3.35	22.5
P9	4.85	5.6	P31	3.95	21.6
P10	0.4	6	P32	5.05	20.85
P11	0.6	7	P33	5.4	22.1
P12	1.8	7.6	P34	3.45	22.8
P13	2.5	8.2	P35	3.75	22.95
P14	9.95	11	P36	4.6	23.55
P15	8.75	11.9	P37	0.7	24.1
P16	9.85	13.5	P38	-0.15	25
P17	9.85	13.7	P39	0.4	31.4
P18	8.65	13.7	P40	1.4	32.2
P19	1.15	21.9	P41	1.05	25.4
P20	2.85	20.5	P42	1.7	27
P21	8.75	15.8	P43	2.05	26.8
P22	9.25	16	P44	2.85	28.3

2. Go to the Quantitative Environmental Learning Project at http://www.seattlecentral.edu/qelp. Choose the Data tab, Ecology links and download DataSet#023 Spokane River Trout Biometrics. Draw the scatter plot for the data set.

$a \times 10^{n}$

1.234×10^{-15}

1.234 E -15

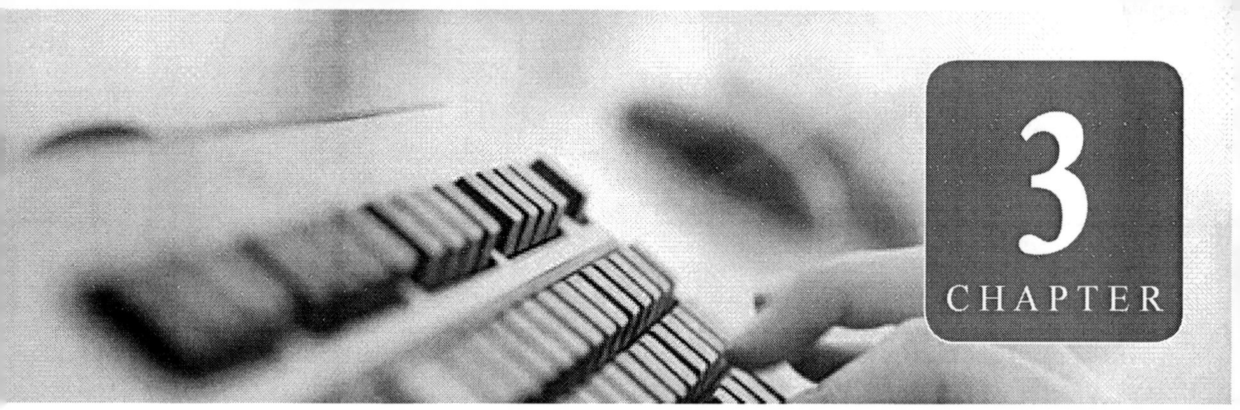

Curve Fitting and Regression

Now that we've seen a picture of our data we might consider whether or not it seems to follow a pattern. Using the scatter plot as a guide we strive to find a familiar graph, such as a line or a known curve like the parabola, that gives a good description of the data even if it's not a perfect fit. We might have several graphs that are reasonable representations of our data, so we want a technique for the finding the best one. Once we have found the best fit we will have an equation that nearly describes the relationship between the two quantities under consideration. We can then use this equation to **estimate** values of y for any valid value of x. The process of fitting data to a known figure such as a line or a parabola is called Regression Analysis.

Each family of geometric objects has the same basic shape and the same general equation, but the numerical values in the equation vary, creating unique aspects of the graph. These numerical values, coefficients of variables or constants are called the **parameters** of the equation. On a line, for example the parameters control how "tilted" the graph is and where it crosses the x-axis. Determining the numerical parameters for an equation, or model, is the main grunt work of regression analysis. We will see that Excel will do that work for us in a very efficient manner.

LINEAR REGRESSION AND THE LINE OF BEST FIT

In looking at the scatter diagram, we are searching for a general shape or tendency that is familiar or well defined. The scatter plot of the Seattle Butter Clams suggests a straight line.

Recall that in order to describe the line we need to find its slope (the measure of the tilt) and its y-intercept, the place where the line crosses the y-axis. Traditionally these values are represented by the letters ***m*** and ***b***, respectively. These are the parameters we will need to find in order to graph the line.

I will use the terms ***x1, y1*** to represent the CELL NAMES where the values of the **first** x and y are located and ***x2, y2*** to represent the CELL NAMES where the values of the **last** x and y are located in the worksheet.

Excel will calculate the slope and intercept by means of the built-in formulas

(3.1) m = SLOPE(yl:y2, x1:x2)

(3.2) b = INTERCEPT(yl:y2, x1:x2)

In the butter clams example two new rows have been inserted to calculate ***m*** and ***b***. The appropriate formula has been placed in cells C1 and C2 as shown in the figure below.

Once the slope and intercept are known, the line of regression or estimating line can be calculated as y = mx +b, or in our case L= mW + b, that is, given the width of a butter clam we can estimate its corresponding length. Note that in cell C5 absolute references are used for the location of ***m*** and ***b*** so that the formula can be replicated down the Linear Estimate Column. Every pair of width and length numbers is related by the same slope and intercept (1.220131 and 0.256895, respectively). In column C, only the location of the width value (column A) changes in each row

	A	B	C
1		slope (m):	1.220131
2		y-intercept (b):	0.256895
3			Linear Estimate
4	W (cm)	L (cm)	L=m*W+b
5	1.3	1.7	1.84
6	1.4	1.9	1.97
7	1.4	1.8	1.97
8	1.5	1.9	2.09
9	1.9	2.3	2.58
10	2.1	3.5	2.82

C1: =SLOPE(B5:B92,A5:A92)

C2: =INTERCEPT(B5:B92,A5:A92)

C5: = $C$1*A5 + $C$2

C9: =$C$1*A9 + $C$2

Table 3.1

In order to add the diagram of the estimating line from column C to the graph:

- Left click on the graph to select it. Choose the Design tab of the Chart Tools Group (or you can RIGHT click directly on the interior white space of existing graph to get a pop-up menu).
- Choose Select Data.
- On the left side of the dialogue box choose **Add** (Series).
- Fill in (or click on) Name, x values (column A - Width entries), y values (column C - Linear Estimates). **Note**: be sure to erase " ={1}" in the y values space.
- Click on OK to close each dialogue box.
- A new series will appear on the chart. Right click on new data points and change chart type to a straight line.

Change the chart Title to reflect the new information. Since there are now 2 data series represented, the actual data and the estimated value, it is helpful to include the legend on the right hand side of the chart. If the legend doesn't currently appear on your chart, add it now:

- Use the Layout tab of the Chart Tools Group (if this group is not visible, left click on the chart).
- Select the Legend labels button.
- Select one of the options to show the legend in the desired location.

One of the benefits of creating a mathematical model is that it can used to estimate results for missing data or future possibilities. For example, in our original data set from Table 2.1, there is no width measurement of 1.7cm. Rather than searching the beach for a clam that is 1.7cm wide we could use the model to estimate that, if a clam is 1.7 cm wide, it would be about 2.33cm long (=$C$1*1.7 + $C$2). The same would be true for a width beyond those measured, say 7.7cm. We could estimate a corresponding length of 9.65cm (=$C$1*7.7 + $C$2).

When the model used is linear, we have an additional measure of goodness of fit. We can calculate a statistic called the sample linear correlation coefficient represented by the letter **r** to see if there is a linear correlation between the two characteristics under consideration. Excel displays **r** using the command

=CORREL(x1:x2, y1:y2).

The value of r will always be in the interval [-1, 1]. A value of 1 is associated with a strictly linear relationship – a line with positive slope. An r value of -1 indicates a perfect line with negative slope. For a sample data set, r will typically be somewhere between the 2 values. The closer r is to ± 1, the stronger the linear relationship. An r value of 0 corresponds to no linear relationship or randomness in the sample. The scatter diagram would look very scattered indeed.

Values around ±0.3 would indicate weak linear relationships. The sign of r should be the same as that of the slope of the regression line.

You have now completed your first mathematical model using linear regression to create an estimate of the length of a Seattle Butter Clam given its width.

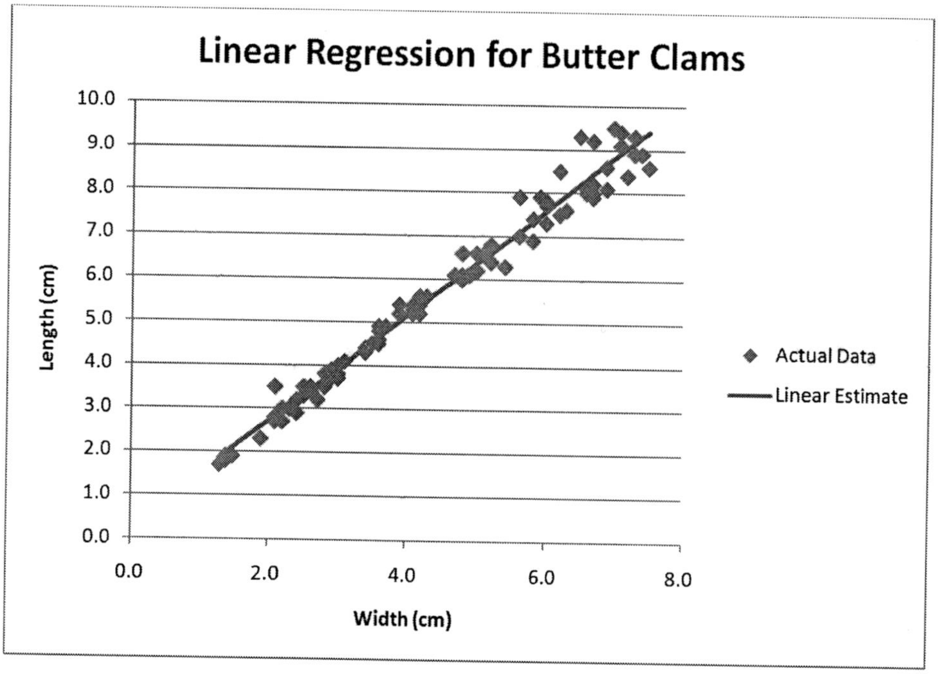

Figure 3.1

NON-LINEAR REGRESSION MODELS

Following the process described in the previous section, let's see what we can find out about possible relationships between the passage of time and speeds for the Men's 400m track event using the following data from the website www.databaseOlympics.com.

First create a scatter plot of the actual data points.

Now we will continue with the linear regression process and see if we can find a straight line that is a good fit for the data.

	A	B	C
1	Olympiad Year	Year	Men's Gold Medal Time
2	1896	0	54.20
3	1900	4	49.40
4	1904	8	49.20
5	1906	10	53.20
6	1908	12	50.00
7	1912	16	48.20
8	1920	24	50.00
9	1924	28	47.60
10	1928	32	47.80
11	1932	36	46.20
12	1936	40	46.50
13	1948	48	46.20
14	1952	52	45.90
15	1956	56	46.70
16	1960	60	44.90
17	1964	64	45.10
18	1968	68	43.86
19	1972	72	44.66
20	1976	76	44.26
21	1980	80	44.60
22	1984	84	44.27
23	1988	88	43.87
24	1992	92	43.50
25	1996	96	43.49
26	2000	100	43.84
27	2004	104	44.00
28	2008	108	43.75

Table 3.2

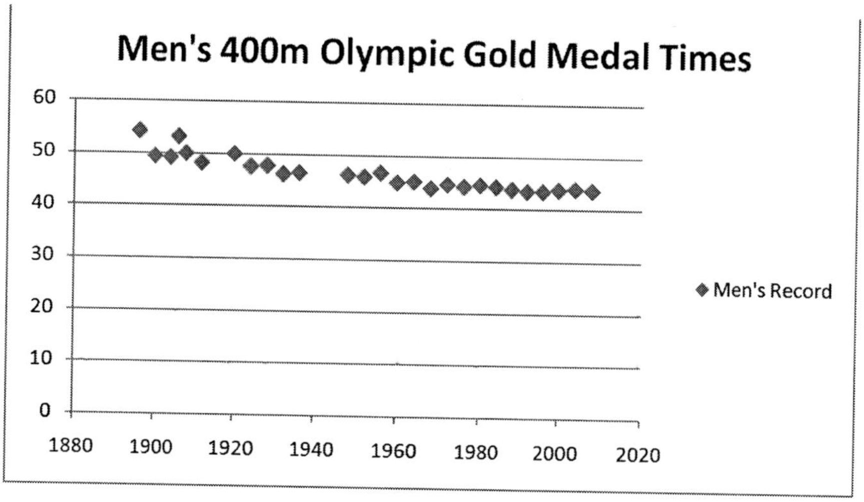

Figure 3.2

Note that accepting the wizard's default format creates a graph in which the data points are bunched together along the top of the graph. So let's make some adjustments. Since the lowest times are all above 40, we can eliminate the empty space at the bottom of the graph by adjusting the scale of the y-axis.

Left click on the graph to select it. The Chart Tools group will become available. Choose the Layout Tab/Axes button/Primary Vertical Axis/More Primary Vertical axis options (the last option in the list).

At the bottom of the Axes Options dialogue box, **Horizontal axis crosses**: change the axis value from 0.00 to 40.00. In a similar way, edit the Primary Horizontal Axis to start at 1880, end at 2020 and use intervals of 20 years. The label associated with the Legend has been changed to indicate that these are the actual data point , using the Chart Tools Group / Design Tab/ Select Data/ Edit option path.

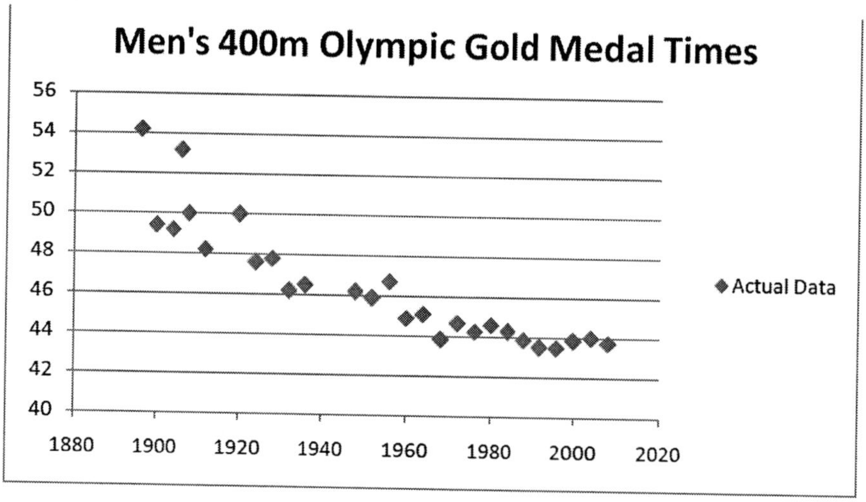

Figure 3.3

A slight adjustment to the x axis will facilitate other model options a little further on in our study. Instead of using the actual year of the olympics lets consider instead the span of years between Olympiads. Letting 1880 = 0, the starting point of the study and continuing to 2008, we have 112 years. We leave it as an exercise for the student to create the linear regression model and add it to the graph as was done in the butter clam example. The result should look similar to the diagram below.

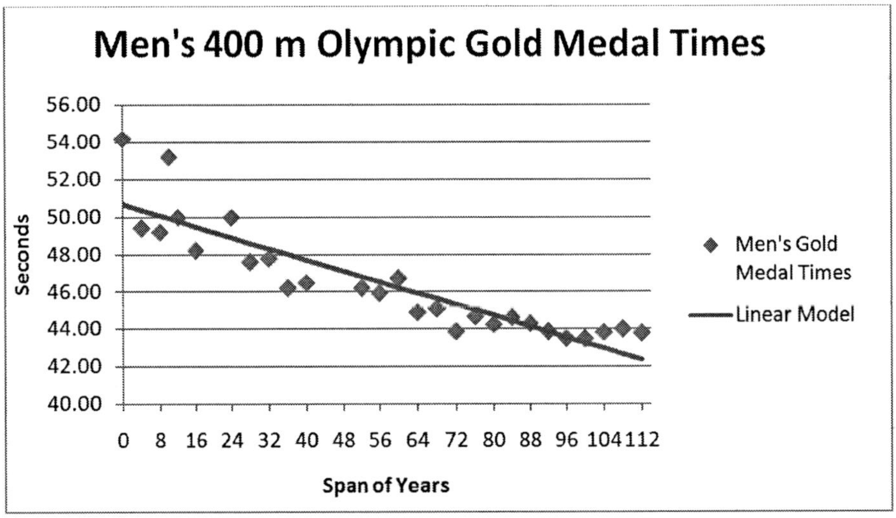

Figure 3.4

The Linear Model diagram suggests that the line gives some general tendencies: as the number of years increases, the time to run the 400 meters decreases. We conclude that the athletes are getting faster. As with the Butter Clams example, we can use the model to fill in gaps in the data. Notice that there is no data for 1916, 1940 or 1944. There were no Olympics held in those years due to World War I and World War II. Had the games been held, we might have expected the 400m event to be run in times of 49.19, 47.41 and 47.11. However, in looking at the far right side of the diagram we would well be skeptical of how accurate any future estimates might be, based on this model. According to the model we would expect a time of 42.07 seconds for 2012. The actual time for this event in 2012 was 43.94.

THE QUADRATIC MODEL

The linear estimates above raise the question "Is there a figure that would give a better fit and more reliable estimates?"

The relationship between the passage of time and the speed at the Olympics has a curvature, the change in the improvement in time is less dramatic from year to year. If the situation were truly linear the decrease in time would be the same from year to year, every year the time is 5 seconds less than the year before, for example. But in the actual data we see large improvements in the early years of the sport that are gradually getting less. In fact we may start to see a pattern that suggests the existence of a lower limit, an amount of time below which the human body cannot possibly run the 400meter event.

We can experiment with other known curves to see how this notion plays out. While the concept of regression for each of these models is essentially the same, the mathematics can be formidable. However, Excel will remove much of the pain by doing the calculations for us.

Let's see what other models might be used. Start by creating a new scatter diagram identical to figure 3.3. We are now ready to experiment with other regression models. On the scatter diagram, right click on a single data point. Choose Trendline. Excel offers several different models for our use. I'm looking for the first part of a parabola, the graph associated with a quadratic equation, something of the form $y = ax^2 + bx + c$. Just as m and b described the line, a,b, and c are the parameters that describe the parabola, determining whether it opens up or down, how wide it is and where it crosses the y-axis.

The quadratic equation is a special case of the polynomial formula, one where the highest degree is 2. So, we will choose Polynomial of order (or degree) 2 in the Trendline dialogue box. In the Trendline Name section choose Custom and fill in a name that is meaningful. I'll use the phrase Quadratic Model. Lastly, to actually see the equation associated with the curve that will appear, check off the box to Display Equation on chart.

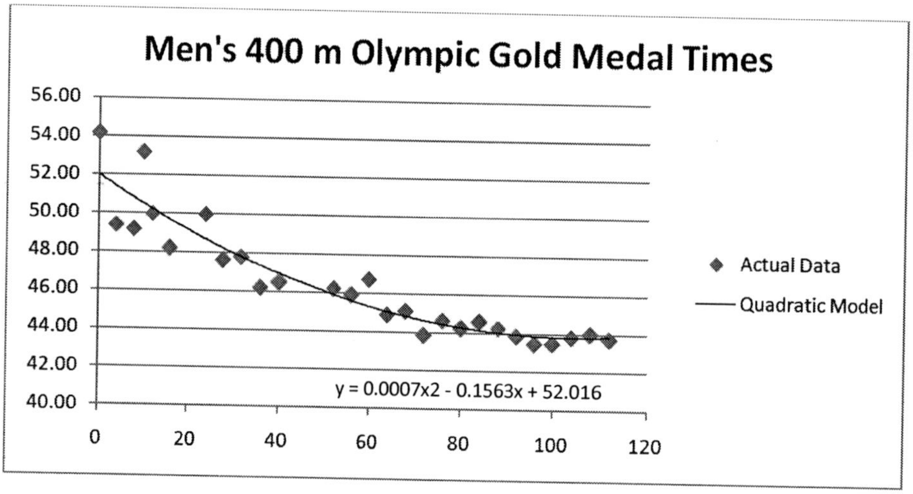

Figure 3.5

In the chart above, the equation appears directly under it's curve, sometimes making it difficult to read. This is simply a text box which you can move to a more convenient location using a click and drag method as shown below.

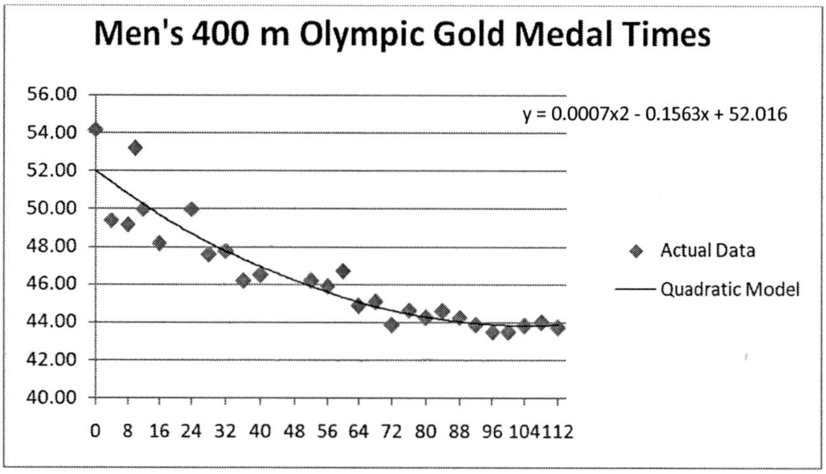

Figure 3.6

We can now add a column to the spreadsheet and enter the equation from the diagram to calculate the values of the quadratic estimates. Using the equation from figure 3.6 above, add a column next to the Linear Model to show the quadratic estimates for each olympiad. Remember to translate the equation into the proper spreadsheet symbols.

=$B$37*B2+$B$38 m is in cell B37, b is in cell B38

= 0.0007*B2^2 - 0.1563*B2 + 52.016

	A	B	C	D	E
1	Olympiad Year	Span of Years	Men's Gold Medal Times	Linear Model	Quadratic Model
2	1896	0	54.20	50.67	52.02
3	1900	4	49.40	50.37	51.40
4	1904	8	49.20	50.08	50.81
5	1906	10	53.20	49.93	50.52
6	1908	12	50.00	49.78	50.24
7	1912	16	48.20	49.48	49.69
8	1920	24	50.00	48.89	48.67
9	1924	28	47.60	48.59	48.19
10	1928	32	47.80	48.30	47.73
11	1932	36	46.20	48.00	47.30
12	1936	40	46.50	47.70	46.88
13	1948	48	46.20	46.81	45.78
14	1952	52	45.90	46.52	45.46
15	1956	56	46.70	46.22	45.16
...	...	...	...	...	...
28	2008	108	43.75	42.53	43.29
29	2012	112	43.94	42.23	43.30

Table 3.3

Using the quadratic model to estimate times for years 1916, 1940 and 1944 yields 49.17, 46.49 and 46.13, respectivley. The quadratic estimate for 2012 is 43.30, which is closer to the actual time than the linear estimate.

We can display both models on the same chart as a visual aide to see the difference in "fit". Create the original linear model as above. Then right-click on of the original data point and choose the option to Add Trendline.

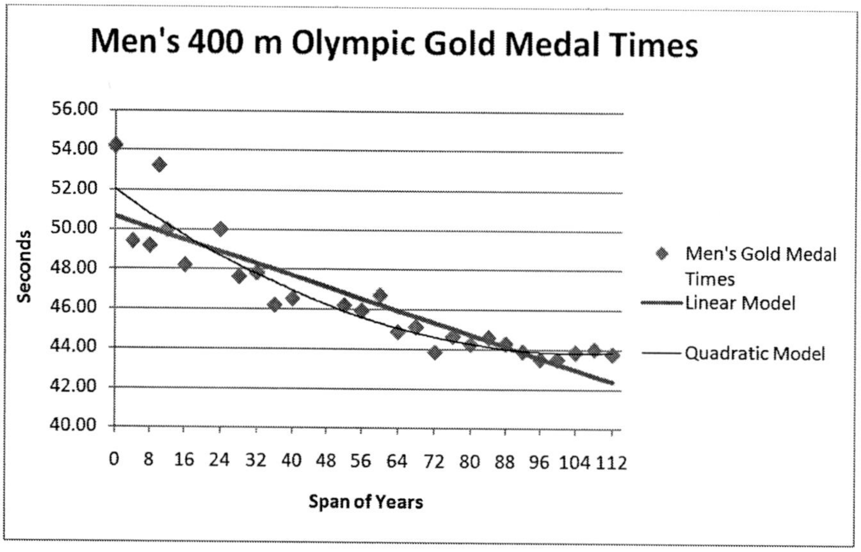

Figure 3.7

DECIDING WHICH MODEL IS BETTER

We have now seen two different models used to represent the same event. Which one is better? We can analyze the data to see which model on average calculates the time that is closest to the actual data. The difference in these two values (actual – estimate) is referred to as a **residual** value. Since some data points are greater than the estimate and some are less than the estimate, we square the differences to neutralize the presence of any negative values. We're interested in distance NOT direction. If we then add up these "squared" values, the smallest sum would represent the model with the overall "best" fit. We could do this process manually, that is, insert additional columns with the square of each residual and then use the SUM function to add them, but Excel provides a built-in function that combines those steps: SUMSQ(*firstCell:lastCell*). This formula is entered in cells F20 and G20 below. Note that the data for 2012 was not included in the analysis but was estimated by the model created up to and including 2008.

	A	B	C	D	E	F	G
1	Olympiad Year	Span of Years	Men's Gold Medal Times	Linear Model	Quadratic Model	Linear Residuals	Quadratic Residuals
2	1896	0	54.20	50.67	52.02	3.53	2.18
3	1900	4	49.40	50.37	51.40	-0.97	-2.00
4	1904	8	49.20	50.08	50.81	-0.88	-1.61
5	1906	10	53.20	49.93	50.52	3.27	2.68
6	1908	12	50.00	49.78	50.24	0.22	-0.24
7	1912	16	48.20	49.48	49.69	-1.28	-1.49
8	1920	24	50.00	48.89	48.67	1.11	1.33
9	1924	28	47.60	48.59	48.19	-0.99	-0.59
10	1928	32	47.80	48.30	47.73	-0.50	0.07
11	1932	36	46.20	48.00	47.30	-1.80	-1.10
12	1936	40	46.50	47.70	46.88	-1.20	-0.38
13	1948	52	46.20	46.81	45.78	-0.61	0.42
14	1952	56	45.90	46.52	45.46	-0.62	0.44
15	1956	60	46.70	46.22	45.16	0.48	1.54
...	...	...	...	...	...	...	...
28	2008	112	43.75	42.36	43.29	1.22	0.28
29	2012	116	43.94	42.07	43.30	1.71	0.43
30							
31					SSR:	43.17	29.87

Sum of Squared Residuals

=SUMSQ(F2:F29)

Best Fit

Table 3.4

We can repeat this process with the other models listed in the Trendline dialogue box. The point is to choose curves that are reasonable and suggest the general pattern that appears in the scatter plot.

It is important to be aware of the domain of the regression model. Decide not only what values of x can be used by the function itself (that is, they are mathematically viable), but also what values of x make sense in the context of the real-world event being modeled. The quadratic model used for the Olympics data is valid for 2012 but the equation actually hits its minimum in the year 2004 and will increase for all future years creating the other side of the parabola.

When using the polynomial model, recall that for a curve of degree n, the curve will turn n-1 times. So a cubic model (degree = 3) may initially decrease, then increases (1 turn), then decrease again (2 turns).

If there is no appropriate line or curve, the x and y values are **independent** of each other. Or you might say that the data represents a **random event.** In this case there should be no pattern evident in the scatter diagram.

EXPONENTIAL GROWTH MODELS

Mathematical modeling is useful to track trends in biological systems such as the growth of a population or the spread of an epidemic. Such phenomena are typically modeled by the use of the exponential function or its inverse, the natural log function.

Here we will consider the Exponential Growth Model, but first take a moment to become familiar with the standard exponential function e^x.

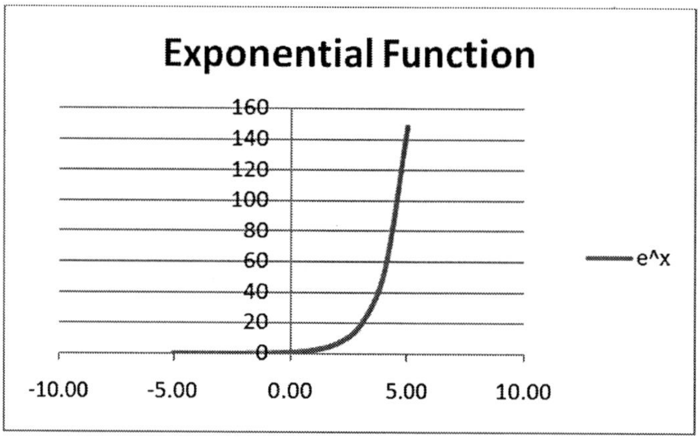

Figure 3.8

The special features of the exponential function are:

- the graph of e^x is always above the x-axis.
- the function increases slowly at first and then quite rapidly.
- the function increases without bound but as x moves to the left e^x approaches 0.
- the graph passes through the point (0, 1), $e^0 = 1$.

Consider the following estimates of the population of North America from 1650 to 2005.http://www.vaughns-1-pagers.com/history/world-population-growth.htm (Note that the years 1970 and 1990 are from http://populationpyramid.net which may account for some of the "wobble" in the scatter plot.)

Year	1650	1750	1800	1810	1820	1830	1840	1850	1860	1870	1880	1890	1900
Population (million)	0.5	3	5.3	7.2	9.6	13	17	23	31	39	50	63	76

Table 3.5 (Continued)

Year	1910	1920	1930	1940	1950	1960	1970	1980	1990	1997	2000	2005
Population (million)	92	105.7	122.7	131.7	150.7	178.5	303.8	372	389.6	464	487	512

Table 3.5

Creating a scatter diagram yields the following graph.

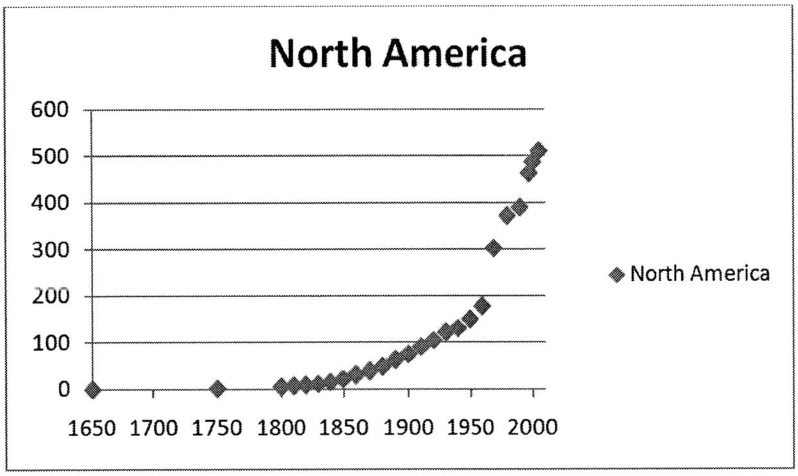

Figure 3.9

Repeat the steps for adding a trendline, choosing the exponential model and its equation.

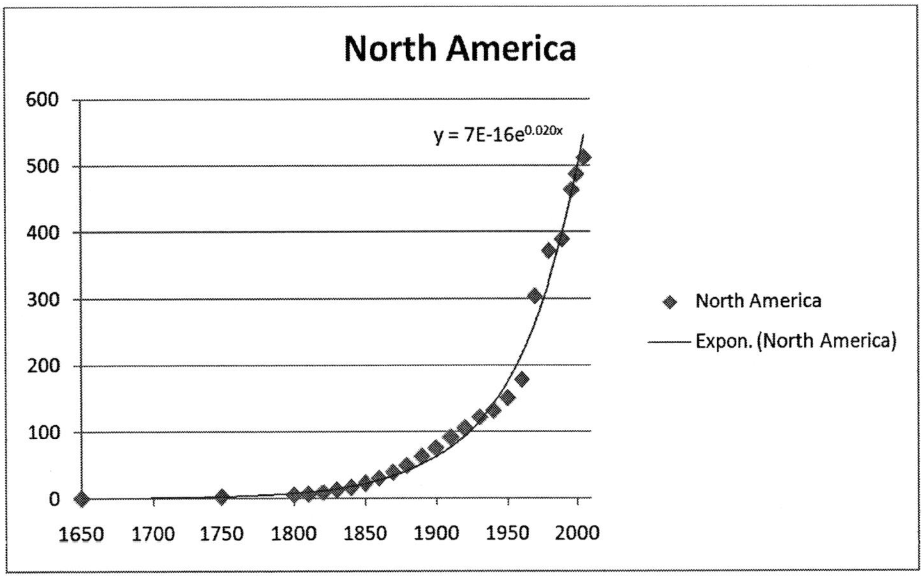

Figure 3.10

The exponential curve is a good representation of the data. We can continue the same type of analysis as was done for the linear and quadratic models, that is, enter the estimating equation and the residual values into the spreadsheet.

The equation given, $y = 7E\text{-}16e^{0.0206x}$ uses scientific notation for the coefficient. 7E-16 is shorthand for a very small number, a decimal followed by 15 zeroes and the number 7: 0.0000000000000007!

The function ae^{bx} is written as the Excel formula =*a**EXP(*b***cell location of x value*).

The exponential function estimates are calculated in column C. As an alternative to putting the values of *a* and *b* directly into the formula, they are placed in their own highlighted cells and an absolute reference to them is used in the formula. Giving parameters their own "space" is a good practice since it highlights the key values for the model and also facilitates "what if" analysis. We simply need to change the value in the parameter box E2, for example, to answer the question: what if the coefficient of x (*b*) is slightly higher?

	A	B	C	D	E	
1	Year	Population (million)	$y = 7E\text{-}16e^{0.0206x}$	Parameters		
2	1650	0.5	0.4	a	b	
3	1750	3	3.2	7.00E-16	0.0206	
4	1800	5.3	8.9 ←			=$D$3*EXP($E$3*A4)
5	1810	7.2	10.9			
6	1820	9.6	13.4			
7	1830	13	16.5			
8	1840	17	20.3			
9	1850	23	24.9			
10	1860	31	30.6			
11	1870	39	37.6			
12	1880	50	46.2			
13	1890	63	56.7			
14	1900	76	69.7			

Table 3.6

We observe that the exponential function is an appropriate model when there is an initial period of slow growth, followed by rapid growth. This model increases without bound. Note that you could also replace the actual year with an index of 0 to 250 as was done with the Olympics data set. The exponential function is used in a great variety of models. In the financial sector, the exponential function is used to calculate continuously compounded interest.

LOGARITHMIC MODELS

If the data suggests an initial rapid growth followed by slower growth, it would probably be better to choose a logarithmic function for the model. Log functions are used to calculate natural phenomena such as the Richter scale for classifying earthquakes, the loudness of sound in decibels and the growth of some epidemics.

The special features of the natural logarithmic function ln(x) are:

- the graph of ln(x) is always to the right of the y-axis
- the function increases rapidly at first and then quite slowly
- as x approaches 0 from the right, ln(x) goes to $-\infty$
- the graph passes through the point (1, 0), ln(1) = 0.

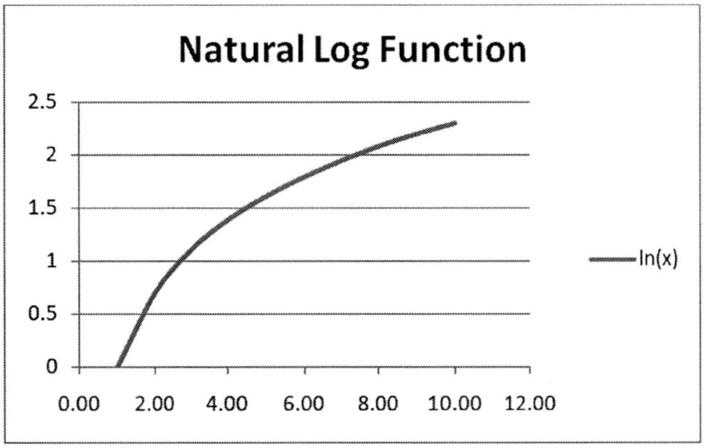

Figure 3.11

DECAY MODELS

Models of diminishment may be represented by a negative exponential function or a negative logarithmic function. Think of these graphs as the "flip" of their positive counterparts. If the coefficient of x (represented by the parameter *b* in the population model) is less than 0, the model is said to be one of Exponential Decay. The half-life of radioactive material is an example of exponential decay.

Below we return to Men's 400m Olympic Gold Medal model from table 3.2. Recall from the discussion on domain at the end of the last section that common sense suggests that there will be a lower limit to the speed at which a human can run 400m. Below is the same data with a negative natural log estimator. The model remains reasonable for limited future projections since – ln(x) decreases very slowly. The time for 2012 would be estimated as 43.75.

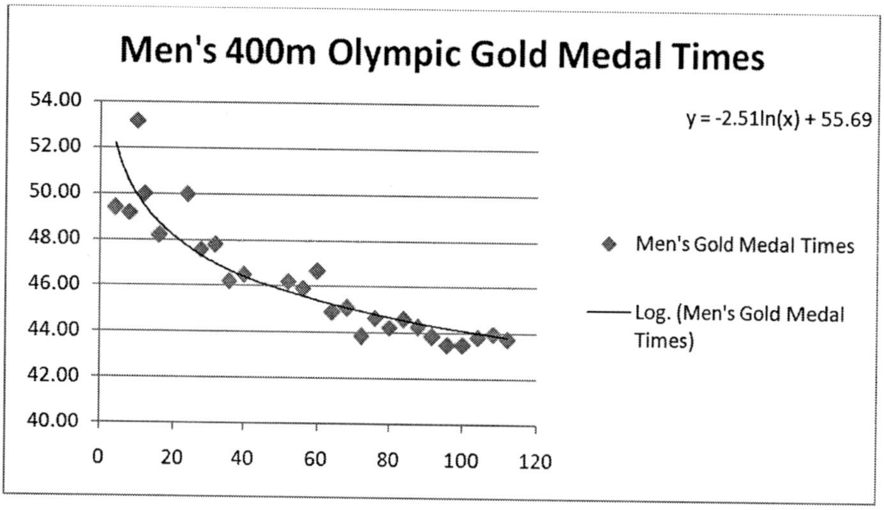

Figure 3.12

Note that whether a model is positive or negative will be determined by Excel, that is, there is only one exponential and one logarithmic option in the trendline dialog box. As a modeler, you should be aware of which model is more appropriate and whether you expect a parameter to be positive or negative. Experiment with several models before deciding which is the best for your purposes. Sometimes you may choose the linear even if it is not the best simply because it is the easiest to use and it is "good enough" for your particular study.

EXERCISES:

1. Go to the Quantitative Environmental Learning Project at http://www.seattlecentral.edu/qelp. Choose the Data tab, Ecology links and download DataSet#023 Spokane River Trout Biometrics. Create a linear, quadratic and exponential regression model. Use the sum of the squared residuals to show which model is the best fit.

2. The women's 400m event was added to the Olympics in 1964. In the first seven Olympiads for this event it appears that the speed of women was improving at a more dramatic rate than that of the men. Using a site like www.databaseOlympics.com, choose Track and Field under the Sports Category, 400m Women, add women's gold medal data for the years 1964 to 1988 to the spreadsheet from this chapter containing the Men's 400m gold medal data.

   a. Do a linear regression using the women's data.

   b. Add the graph of the women's line to the same set of axis as the men. If needed change the scale of the y-axis to give a better fit.

   c. Find the correlation coefficient for each model (Men and Women). Is the linear model valid? Why or why not?

d. Using these models, predict when women will outrun men. Do you believe this?

e. Create a new graph that contains just the two regression lines, showing the intersection (i.e., the point where women outrun men.)

f. Create a Word Document that contains the summary of your answers and a copy of the two graphs.

3. On a new worksheet, copy the raw data for men and women used in exercise 2, then add the women's data from 1992 to the present.

   a. Create non-linear models for the full set of men and women's data.

   b. Find the residuals for each model. Which model has the better fit for men? Which has the better fit for women? Why?

   c. Use the models to predict what the times for each would be in the next Olympics.

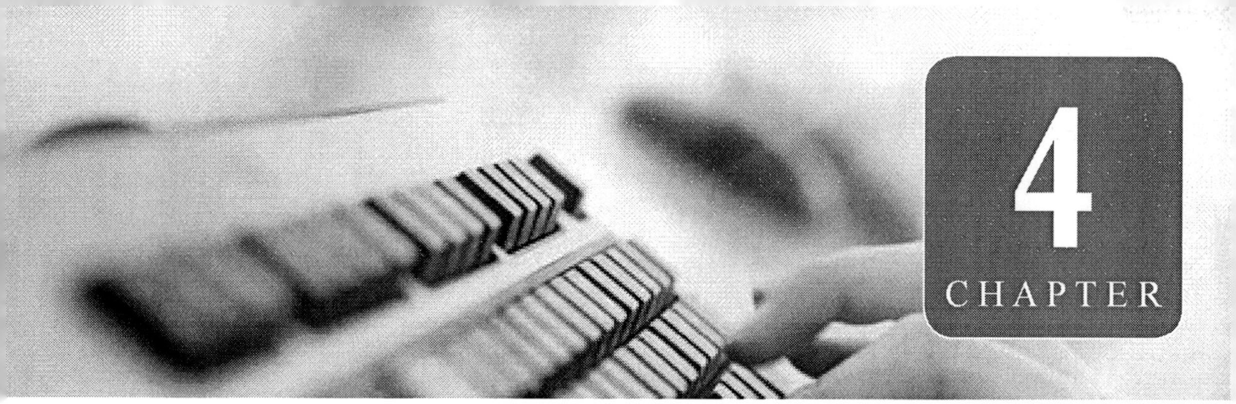

Data Manipulation

Data can be gathered and stored in many forms: html files from the web, tables in Word documents, raw data stored in a variety of formats such as rows of data separated by tabs or commas or spaces. Data might also be stored in a special format created by a particular software package. Excel provides an excellent environment in which to transfer data between otherwise incompatible formats. The names of files consisting exclusively of data items often have 3-letter extensions that indicate the format of the data. For example, you might see the extension ".csv". Excel recognizes this type of file as one that contains data separated by commas (literally: "comma separated values"). Sometimes the extension will just be ".txt" meaning the file contains **text** but the format is not specified.

Any keyboard character that can be used to separate one piece of data from the next is called a **delimiter**. Common delimiters are commas, tabs, semicolons, or one or more spaces sometimes referred to as "white space".

Before you try to transfer data from one environment to another, spend some time looking at the data to determine the delimiters that are in use. When using other software applications such as database management programs, statistics packages, or any software that uses tables to organize information, look to see if there is a built-in conversion program. The best place to look is on the main menu, typically in a "File" tab or category. Look for an "External Data" or "Export Data" option and follow the instructions to create the desired data file format.

Another possibility for data conversion is to check the "Save As" option for your file. Very often Excel or Comma Separated Value will be listed in the "Save as type" line of the dialogue box.

You might also achieve the desired retrieval of information by simply using a copy/ paste (or paste special) sequence of commands.

Some data might be available, but several categories may all be dumped into one column. We need a mechanism to efficiently separate the categories. This process is called **parsing** the data.

Suppose for example you find the information in table 4.1 about record holders for the men's mile online (see, for example, http://en.wikipedia.org/wiki/Mile_run_world_record_progression). You copy and paste a partial list into Excel, but all the data is copied into one column. It would be much more versatile to have the data in three separate columns: Year, First, Last. You could do a tedious series of cut and paste commands but if you have a long list, this process would get old very fast!

1875 (Walter Slade)
1894 (Fred Bacon)
1923 (PaavoNurmi)
1937 (Sidney Wooderson)
1942 (GunderHagg)
1945 (GunderHagg)
1954 (Roger Bannister)
1964 (Peter Snell)
1967 (Jim Ryun)
1975 (John Walker)
1979 (Sebastian Coe)
1980 (Steve Ovett)
1985 (Steve Cram)
1993 (NoureddineMorceli)

Table 4.1

Instead let's use Excel to once again remove as much of the tedium as possible.

Steps to Parse Data:

1. Select the data to be parsed: left click and drag to highlight the desired selection.
2. Choose the Data tab/Text to Columns icon in the Data Tools group.
3. Select Delimited as the Original data type. You will see an updated preview for each selection you make. Click on Next >.

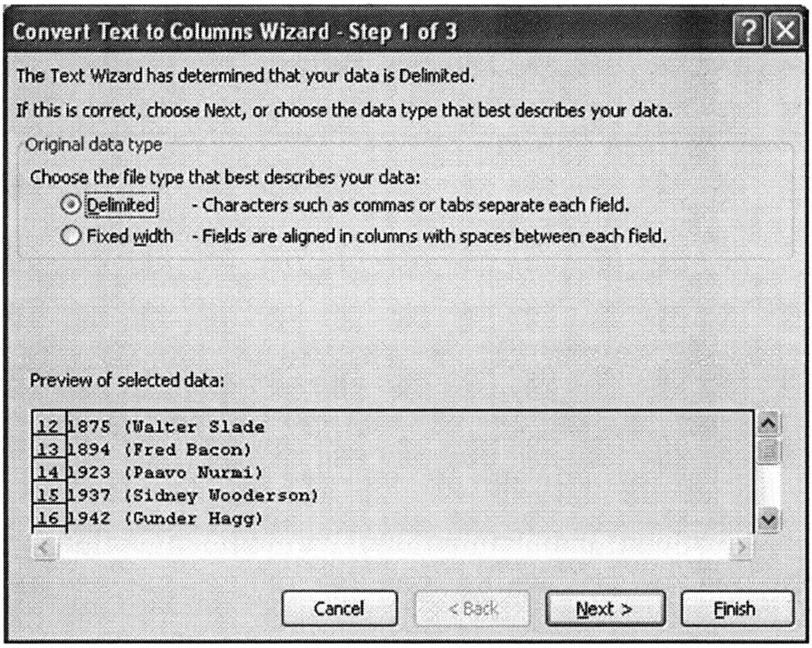

Figure 4.1

4. Check off one or more delimiters: in this case we select Space and Other to enter "(" as a delimiter for the name data. Also check the box "Treat consecutive delimiters as one". If any entry has more than one space between the year and name any extra spaces will be ignored.

   Click on "Next >".

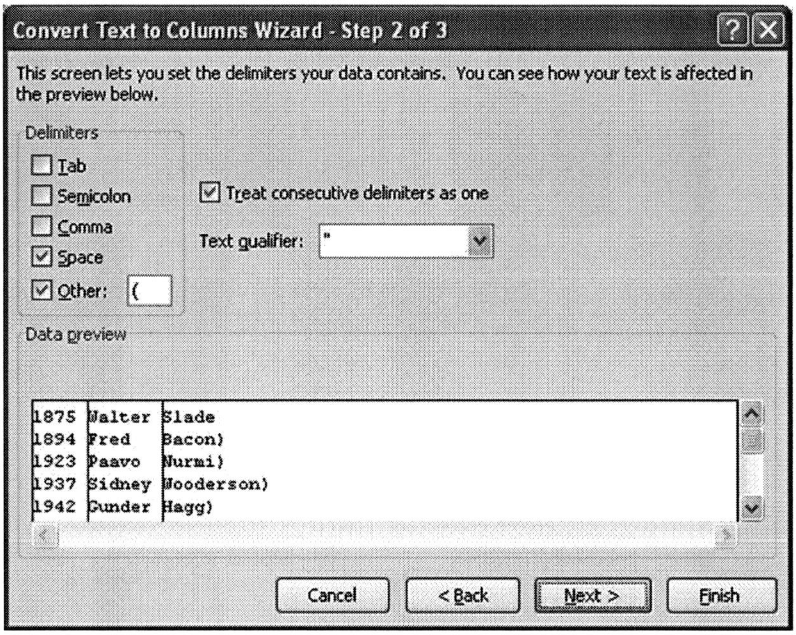

Figure 4.2

You will now have the opportunity to look at each column (by clicking on it) and verifying the type of data format (General, Text, etc.) General is the default type. The Advanced... button will allow you to include additional details for the format for numeric data.

When you are satisfied with the format of each column, CHOOSE THE DESTINATION CELL. This is the cell address of the upper left corner of the new location in the spreadsheet for the parsed data. The default here is the starting value of the original data which will be overwritten in the process. If you choose a different location, for example NEXT TO the original, you will have a copy of both formats. This is sometimes helpful in case the resulting table is not what you intended and you want to try parsing the data again. You can always delete the original data when you are satisfied with the end result. In the example below the original data starts in cell F12 and ends in cell F25. The new data will start in cell G12 and end in cell I25.

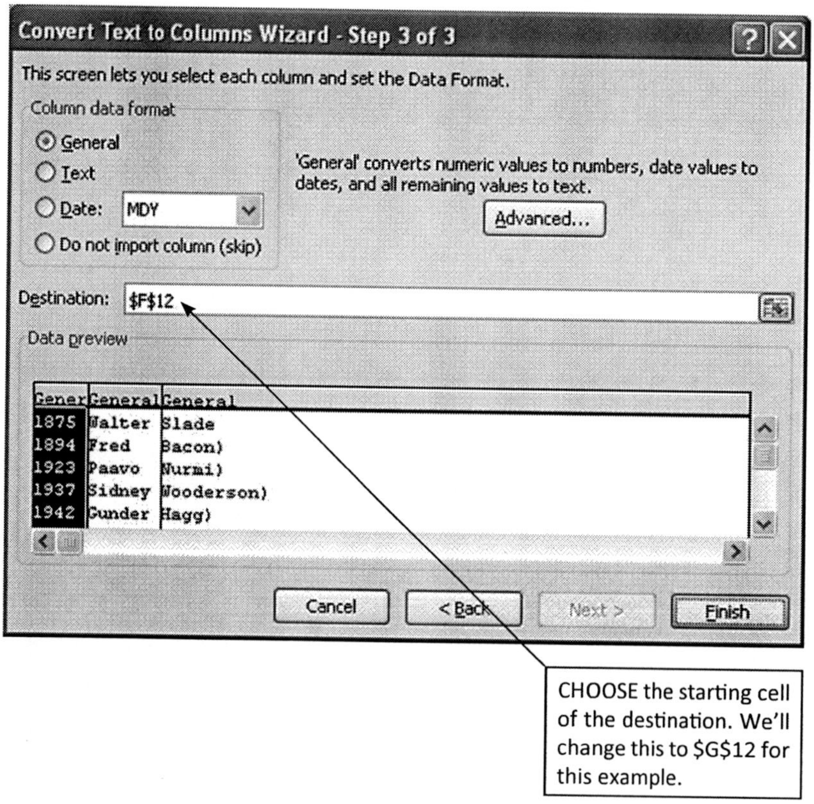

Figure 4.3

Click on Finish. The results are the following:

	F	G	H	I
12	1875 (Walter Slade)	1875	Walter	Slade)
13	1894 (Fred Bacon)	1894	Fred	Bacon)
14	1923 (PaavoNurmi)	1923	Paavo	Nurmi)
15	1937 (Sidney Wooderson)	1937	Sidney	Wooderson)
16	1942 (GunderHagg)	1942	Gunder	Hagg)
17	1945 (GunderHagg)	1945	Gunder	Hagg)
18	1954 (Roger Bannister)	1954	Roger	Bannister)
19	1964 (Peter Snell)	1964	Peter	Snell)
20	1967 (Jim Ryun)	1967	Jim	Ryun)
21	1975 (John Walker)	1975	John	Walker)
22	1979 (Sebastian Coe)	1979	Sebastian	Coe)
23	1980 (Steve Ovett)	1980	Steve	Ovett)
24	1985 (Steve Cram)	1985	Steve	Cram)
25	1993 (NoureddineMorceli)	1993	Noureddine	Morceli)

Table 4.2

We have one last step to clean up the resulting data set. Note that in the last column every name is followed by ")". To remove these extra characters do a "find and replace" edit. That is, first select the column of last names, then choose the Home tab. The Editing group is on the right side of the ribbon. Choose the Find & Select dropdown menu. Choose Replace... In the Find what space type ")". Replace with: leave this blank since we don't want anything added.

Choose Replace All. The closing parenthesis is removed from the last names and we now have three distinct, clean fields of data.

Sometimes it is desirable to put fields together in one column. The opposite of parsing is a process call concatenation. Suppose, for instance, that we are creating a mailing list using the names in Table 4.2. We'd like to store the mailing title without any extra spacing such as Mr. Walter Slade. We can add a formula in column J that combines the title "Mr" and the contents of columns H and I. This process is call **concatenation** and is achieved using the & symbol. The formula in cell J12 would be

= **"Mr." & H12 & " " & I12**

Note that you must provide the space inside the first phrase "Mr." as well as the space between the first and last name.

SORTING AND FILTERING DATA

Once your data is properly parsed, you can rearrange it in a particular order or you can filter out particular values in a column. These techniques become very valuable when data sets are large and not easily scanned manually.

As an example, let's alphabetize the athletes by last name. We are continuing to use editing functions found on the Home tab and Editing Group. Select the 3 columns of data including the year, first and last names. Choose the Sort & Filter dropdown menu. Choose Custom Sort and Sort by Column I (the location of the last names). The contents of all three columns will be rearranged so that each athlete's information remains together but now in alphabetical order.

YEAR	FIRST	LAST
1894	Fred	Bacon
1954	Roger	Bannister
1979	Sebastian	Coe
1985	Steve	Cram
1942	Gunder	Hagg
1945	Gunder	Hagg
1993	Noureddine	Morceli
1923	Paavo	Nurmi
1980	Steve	Ovett
1967	Jim	Ryun
1875	Walter	Slade
1964	Peter	Snell
1975	John	Walker
1937	Sidney	Wooderson

Table 4.3

We can also filter the above data, that is, use a particular criterion to show only the records that match the characteristic(s) we choose. Once again choose the Sort & Filter dropdown menu. This time select Filter. The first value in each column now has a drop-down arrow next to it. By clicking on these arrows we can choose specific values to view. In the last name column remove the check to Select all and check off just Haag instead. Only the two rows with Gunder Hagg's information are visible. Note that the data is still in the same location in the spreadsheet, the other rows have been temporarily hidden. The filter is an on-off toggle switch. By returning to the Sort & Filter menu and choosing Filter again, the switch is turned off.

Sometimes changing the order of data, or looking at specific subsets of data can give us new insights or raise new questions to pursue.

EXERCISES

Go to the NYC Open Data website https://nycopendata.socrata.com/data.

Choose the 311 tile icon. Note the multicolored options list on the right side of the window. The data can be filtered by clicking on the menu button (next to i) in each category.

In order to scale down the amount of data:

- In the agency column choose any one agency as the filter.
- In the incident zip code column choose any 1 zip code as the filter.
- Using the Manage option from the multicolored list, go through the list and uncheck all columns except Unique Key, Created Date and Agency.
- Choose the Export option from the multicolored list. Use the xls or xlsx format and save the file to your computer.
- Open the new file. The information we are interested in is the Created Date. However, we would like separate columns for Month, Day, Year, Time, AM/PM. The time element is present even though it may not be visible in the column. If you choose a cell in this column you'll see the time in the function bar.
- Choose the first 100 or so records (there may be thousands of rows in the file.)
- Parse the data into 5 new columns: Month, Day, Year, Time, AM/PM

  Some sample records are shown below:

Created Date	Month	Day	Year	Time	AM/PM
12/05/2013	12	5	2013	4:29:22	PM
12/04/2013	12	5	2013	12:25:52	PM
12/02/2013	12	4	2013	2:39:13	PM
12/02/2013	12	2	2013	9:52:33	PM
12/02/2013	12	2	2013	7:33:35	PM
11/28/2013	12	2	2013	5:01:50	PM

Basic Statistics

USING ARRAY FUNCTIONS

In the following chapter we will employ the use of several functions that are designated as "Array Functions", that is the function returns more than one result or an array of answers. The method for these functions generally follows the same pattern, which deviates from the formula replication we have used in the earlier chapters.

When using array functions, you first have to decide exactly how much space is needed for the answers. You execute the function in the following manner:

1. Select the cells where the results will be stored.
2. Type in the formula, either in the formula bar or by starting the formula with the = symbol.
3. When you have finished typing the formula DO NOT PRESS ENTER!

Instead hold down the **Shift** and **Ctrl** keys, then press **Enter**. In the following pages this step will be designated by the notation **[Shift + Ctrl + Enter]**.

All of the answer cells will be filled in and the formula will appear with { } around the command indicating an array function. The curly braces are provided by the system and cannot be entered manually by the user. The particular array function in use will be explained in the section where it is introduced.

Statistical Measures

Now that you have seen some methods for determining patterns in data, we turn our attention to methods for summarizing data. If a data set contains all possible values of a characteristic being studied it is called a **population**. A subset of a population is called a **sample**. Typically samples are gathered by actually counting or measuring items in an experiment. The sample values can be summarized by numbers, called **statistics**, that capture the general essence of the data for large data sets rather than looking at individual measurements. Some of the characteristics we can use to summarize sets of data fall into the following categories. At a glance some of the most common measures are:

A. Measures of Central Tendency: these measurements look for numbers that are in the center of a data set. They include the Mean or average, the Median or middle score when scores are sorted in order of value, the Mode or score that occurs most often.

B. Measures of Dispersion: Range or width of the data and Standard Deviation which measures distance from the mean.

C. Measures of Location: when data is arranged in order, it can be separated into groups of equal sized members. The numbers that are the boundaries of those groups are Quartiles (4 equal groups), Deciles (10 equal groups), Percentiles (100 equal groups). The Median is also a measure of location. It is the middle score splitting the set into 2 equal groups.

Excel easily handles the above measurements with a robust collection of built-in formulas listed below. The basic techniques from Chapter 1 can be employed to click and drag the collection of cells that contain the data. You may have already seen some of the formulas in Chapter 1 as well. They are listed here for the sake of convenience and completeness.

Measures of Central Tendency

The first 2 commands are very straight forward:

Mean: = AVERAGE(*startCell:endCell*)

Median: = MEDIAN(*startCell:endCell*)

Starting with Excel 2010 the MODE function has been expanded. There may be more than one mode in a data set. The MODE.SNGL command returns just the first value. It is equivalent to the MODE formula in earlier versions of Excel, which is also included in the 2010 version for backward compatibility.

Mode: = MODE.SNGL(*startCell:endCell*)

A second mode function will display multiple modes if they exist:

= MODE.MULT(*startCell:endCell*) ⋆

⋆This is an array function and is executed as described in the beginning of this chapter. The tricky part about executing the MODE.MULT command is that you don't know how many places to reserve for the answer. If you know you only want the first 2 or 3 modes, then just reserve the required 2 or 3 cells for the result. If you are trying to see how many modes may exist, be generous in reserving more space than you think will be required. When the command is executed, the modes will be listed in numerical order and the message **#N/A** (**N**ot **A**vailable) will be displayed in any remaining cells. Be advised that the #NA command cannot be deleted since it is part of the array of results. You would have to delete the entire command and redo it with the exact number of response cells to "clean up" the spreadsheet.

Measures of Dispersion

Excel 2010 also introduced several forms for the calculation of standard deviation. We will just illustrate that of the standard deviation for a sample set of data – scores that have actually been measured.

Standard Deviation: = STDEV.S(*startCell:endCell*)

Note that this is equivalent to STDEV(*startCell:endCell*) in earlier versions of Excel.

Range: the range must be calculated with a user defined function. It is the highest score – lowest, but we can use built-in functions to determine what those scores are.

= MAX(*startCell:endCell*) - MIN(*startCell:endCell*)

Measures of Location

As with the other measures, Excel offers variations on measures of location. We will illustrate just a few. The commands here all have counterparts in earlier versions of Excel – just drop the INC extension. The QUARTILE.INC and PERCENTILE.INC commands give the value of the number that splits the data set into the desired number of subdivisions.

Quartiles: =QUARTILE.INC(*startCell:endCell, quartileNumber*)

This command is equivalent to the earlier version Excel command QUARTILE.

The second parameter is the location of the desired quartile 1, 2, 3. The values 0 and 4 can be used to find the minimum and maximum, respectively.

Percentiles: =PERCENTILE.INC(*startCell:endCell,percentNumber*)

It is important to note here that the *percentNumber* must be written as a decimal value. For example, for an array of cells from B1 to B20 the commands : =QUARTILE. INC(B1:B201, 1) and =PERCENTILE.INC(B1:B20, .25) are equivalent.

To find the percentile value of a particular score in a data set use the PERCENTRANK command: =PERCENTRANK.INC(*startCell:endCell, score, [decimalPlaces]*)

You can specify a third optional parameter for the desired number of decimal places in the resulting percentile. The default is 3.

Frequency Tables and Histograms

In Chapter 2 we saw what the pattern of the data looked like when each data point was represented. Now we will investigate what the data looks like when we group it into subsets. We want to see how often a score falls into a certain subset. We refer to this as **frequency**.

The following example is from the World Health Organization (www.who.int/research/en). On the WHO website use the "Data and statistics" tab then click the Data link under "Mortality and global health estimates" heading.

In the list entitled “in this section” choose the Life expectancy link, and Life expectancy again in the next screen. Click on the “Show filters” button to fine tune your choice of data categories. For the following example I used **Indicator**: Life expectancy at birth, **Year**: 2011, **Sex**: both sexes. I did not filter on **WHO region** or **Country** so that all 194 countries would be represented in the resulting table.

Press the Apply button to create your customized table. The filtered data will be shown. You can save this in various formats. Choose Excel spreadsheet.

This site is regularly updated and the particular steps may vary from time to time, but there is usually a very good system for choosing and downloading data.

Several worksheets are downloaded in the workbook. We will use the Data page only. In this version numbers are given as both text and numerical formats. Remember to verify the data type before attempting to do any calculations (See Chapter 4 for the process). Eliminate any columns that are not needed or of interest in this study. For the sake of illustration both columns of numbers are shown, but we will eliminate the text version before beginning.

A sample of the resulting table is shown next.

Excel places a green indicator in the corner of each entry in columns A and D to warn that these values are stored as text not as numbers. There are 194 countries in the data set.

	A	B	C	D	E
1	Year	WHO region	Country	Display Value	Numeric Value
2	2011	Eastern Mediterranean	Afghanistan	60	60
3	2011	Europe	Albania	74	74
4	2011	Africa	Algeria	73	73
5	2011	Europe	Andorra	82	82
6	2011	Africa	Angola	51	51
7	2011	Americas	Antigua and Barbuda	75	75
8	2011	Americas	Argentina	76	76
9	2011	Europe	Armenia	71	71
10	2011	Western Pacific	Australia	82	82
11	2011	Europe	Austria	81	81
12	2011	Europe	Azerbaijan	71	71
13	2011	Americas	Bahamas	75	75
14	2011	Eastern Mediterranean	Bahrain	79	79
15	2011	South-East Asia	Bangladesh	70	70
16	2011	Americas	Barbados	78	78
17	2011	Europe	Belarus	71	71
18	2011	Europe	Belgium	80	80

Table 5.1

The summary statistics discussed above are

	A	B	C	D
1	SUMMARY STATISTICS			
2	Mean	70.01		
3	Median	72.50		
4	Mode	74.00		
5				
6	Max	83.00		
7	Min	47.00		
8	Range	36.00		
9	StdDev	9.26		
10				
11	Quartiles:	1st	2nd	3rd
12		61.00	72.50	76.00

Table 5.2

The formulas are shown below. Remember that you can have Excel display formulas by toggling the CTRL ` (the grave accent mark located above the tab key on the left side of the keyboard.)

SUMMARY STATISTICS			
Mean	=AVERAGE($E$2:$E$195)		
Median	=MEDIAN($E$2:$E$195)		
Mode	=MODE.SNGL(E2:E195)		
Max	=MAX(E2:E195)		
Min	=MIN(E2:E195)		
Range	=I6-I7		
StdDev	=STDEV.S(E2:E195)		
Quartiles:	1st	2nd	3rd
	=QUARTILE. INC($E$2:$E$195,1)	=QUARTILE. INC($E$2:$E$195,2)	=QUARTILE. INC($E$2:$E$195,3)

Table 5.3

Let's now create a picture of the data. We know that the range is 36 with a minimum of 47 and a maximum of 83. We will create a ***column chart*** that groups the data in intervals based on these numbers. Since there are 36 numbers represented, let's split the data into groups that each have a width of 6. The number of groups is arbitrary, but typically you should use at least 5 to get a good description of the data and a maximum of 20. This part of the process is very subjective and you should feel free to experiment with both the width and number of intervals you decide to use. The important part is that the width of every group is the same and that the number of intervals captures all the data.

Computer applications call these groups **bins** and the process of creating the groups is referred to as "binning". Think of it as having a series of boxes into which you place each country depending on its life expectancy. When every country has been placed, we count the number of countries in each box or bin. This number is referred to as the **frequency**. We will then create a column chart which is a frequency diagram or **histogram**.

After some experimentation, I've chosen to start with the number 46, just below lowest value, 47. Create a bin that will contain 6 numbers (46, 47, 48, 49, 50, 51). Continue creating the groups, making sure that each is the same width, and that both the minimum and the maximum of the data set are included in the intervals. Notice that there is no overlap in the intervals. In all there are 7 class intervals as shown below in table 5.4. The INTERVALS column below is used to create labels for the diagram. Excel is only interested in the upper value of each interval, labeled BINS below. There is a built-in function to count the frequencies, but note that it is an **array function** and must be executed as stated in the beginning of the chapter. We will go through the process step by step here. The command is

=FREQUENCY(*range of data cell, range of bin cells*).

The following example uses the data on life expectancy that we downloaded and displayed above in Table 5.1.

When you have decided on the intervals (column G), place just the upper limit in the bins (column H). Click and drag to selected cells I16 to I22, the location for the resulting frequencies. Once the destination cells have been selected, type the formula

=FREQUENCY(E2:E195, H16:H22)

Range of data cells   Range of bin cells

	G	H	I
15	INTERVALS	BINS	FREQUENCY
16	46-51	51	10
17	52-57	57	15
18	58-63	63	23
19	64-69	69	29
20	70-75	75	57
21	76-81	81	44
22	82-87	87	16
23		Total:	194

Table 5.4

REMEMBER: DO NOT PRESS ENTER!

Hold down the Shift and Ctrl keys, <u>then</u> press Enter. [Ctrl+Shift+Enter]

Cells I16 to I22 will be filled with the frequency for each corresponding bin.

To draw the Frequency diagram, select the Frequency column ONLY. Choose the Insert tab of the main menu bar and choose **Column** in the Charts group of the ribbon. Select a 2-D Column. The default labels for the columns will be 1, 2, 3, etc. To change these values to those in the INTERVALS column use the Chart Tools group/Select Data option. Edit the HORIZONTAL Axis Labels on the right side of the dialogue box and enter cells G16:G22 from the INTERVALS column.

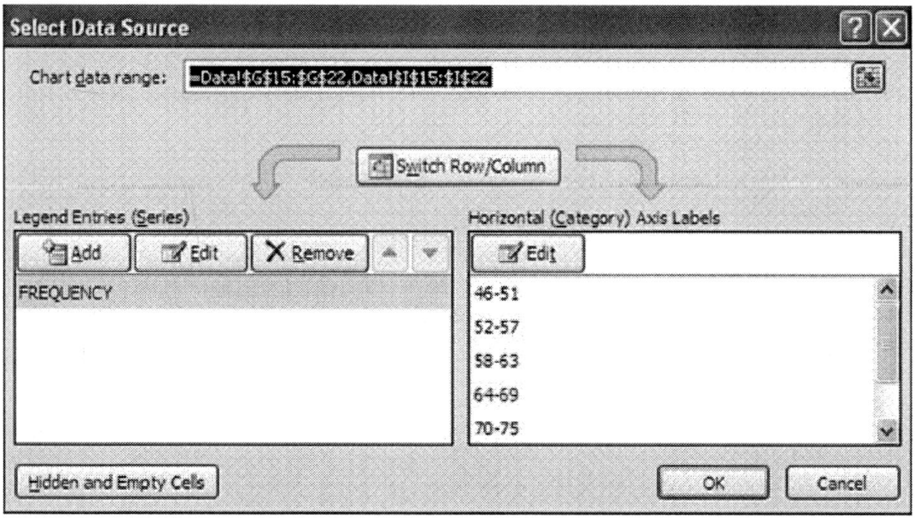

Figure 5.1

The Frequency diagram should look something like

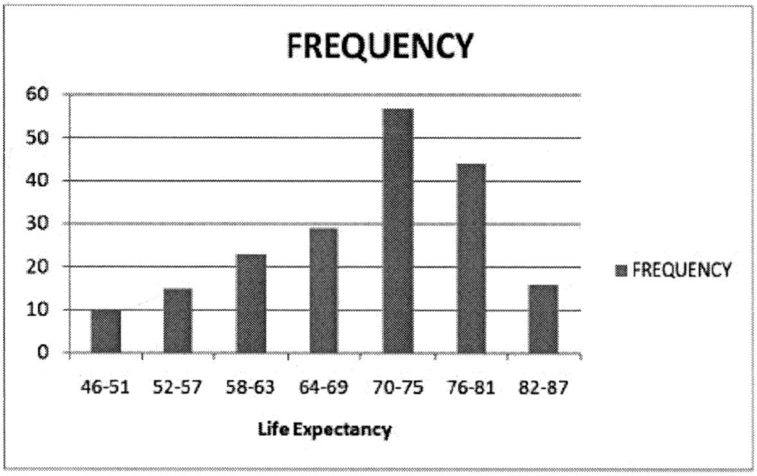

Figure 5.2

It is unfortunate that Excel refers to this figure as a Column Chart. Mathematicians typically refer to charts consisting of vertical columns as bar charts. Excel uses the term bar charts to represent data horizontally. The width of the bars can be increased to draw a proper histogram by double clicking one of the bars. A format box will pop up. Adjust the Gap Width to 0% or 1%. If you use 0% also change the color of the border to give contrast between the bars.

DEDICATED STATISTICS PACKAGES

The above exercise illustrates that while spreadsheets have many excellent features, there are times when a considerable amount of effort is required to achieve the desired results. However, there are many application software programs that have been written for various fields in mathematics. There are several programs written specifically for statistics, SPSS, SAS, and R to name a few. Let's repeat the exact same analysis of Life Expectancy using IBM SPSS Statistics 19.

First we need to import the data from Excel into the SPSS environment. It is best if you start with a clean version of the spreadsheet, that is make a copy and remove any extra pages that were created during the download from the WHO website. Also delete the graph and summary statistics from the Data sheet. It will be easier to import columns of data only. Note that in the spreadsheet the headings of the columns are in the first row of the spreadsheet. SPSS will ask us about headings during the import process.

Open the SPSS program. On the opening dialog box or in the main file menu, choose the option to open a data source. The default type is ".sav", the extension used by SPSS for its own data files. Choose the appropriate folder where the Life Expectancy workbook is stored. Then click the dropdown menu on the "Files of type" line and select Excel. Open the file. Be sure to check the option "Read variable names from the first row of data". You can specify a particular worksheet and range of cells, but if you have created a copy of the workbook containing only data, you can just accept the default values.

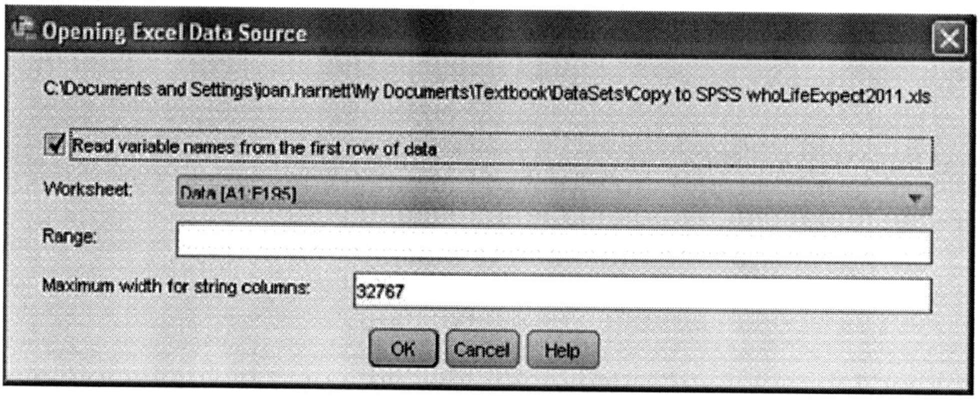

Figure 5.3

Let's take a moment to become familiar with the SPSS environment. First, notice that SPSS uses a separate screen to report all output. This includes the summary statistics and graphs that were stored within the spreadsheet in Excel. We will say more about this window when we do our analysis.

Data management programs store 2 different aspects of data, its actual value and information about the data's type (text, integer, real numbers, etc.). The data values appear on the "Data View" tab of SPSS Data Editor Window, but the information about the data, called **meta-data**, is stored on the page labeled "Variable View". The storage area of meta-data may also be referred to as a data dictionary.

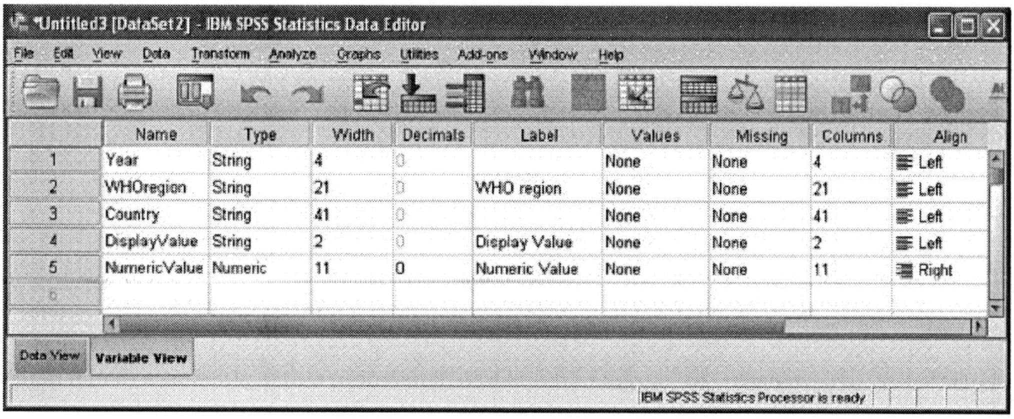

	Name	Type	Width	Decimals	Label	Values	Missing	Columns	Align
1	Year	String	4	0		None	None	4	Left
2	WHOregion	String	21	0	WHO region	None	None	21	Left
3	Country	String	41	0		None	None	41	Left
4	DisplayValue	String	2	0	Display Value	None	None	2	Left
5	NumericValue	Numeric	11	0	Numeric Value	None	None	11	Right
6									

Figure 5.4

When you click on certain cells, you may see a drop-down arrow or a "build" button.

These are indicators that other options exist. You may edit most entries. Each category of data (column or field) has the following attributes:

- Name: this was the first row of the Excel spreadsheet. If you did not have headings, a generic name such as Var1 will be assigned.
- Type: this category specifies that the data contains characters (String) or numbers (Numeric). Numeric data will have a variety of format options.
- Width: the number of digits or characters in the largest entry.
- Decimals: the number of decimal places if the item is numeric.
- Label: this is a word or phrase that will show up in reports or when the mouse hovers over the variable name in the Data View.
- Values: this attribute can be used to specify and label categories of data using codes. For example, if the variable is Gender, then values might be 0 = Male, 1 = Female.
- Missing: in some statistical studies, for example a survey, there may be some cells that arc blank or have values that are missing. You may assign a default or dummy value to be used.
- Columns: the width of the columns in the Data View.
- Align: the alignment of data in the cells of the Data View.

- Measure: data may represent a name, like that of a country, and is called **Nominal** or it may imply an ordering (small, med, lge, or 1, 2, 3) and is called **Ordinal** or it may be intended for calculations and is called **Scale.** Some statistical processes will require a particular type of data in order to be executed. If an item of data is nominal, it makes no sense to find an average.
- Role: this attribute can be used to pre-select a variable for analysis. It is beyond the scope of what we will address in this text.

Let's return to the Data View worksheet and do the same analysis as we had done earlier in Excel. We will use a very small portion of the statistical processes that are available but it should be a sufficient sampling to give you an appreciation for the use of dedicated software.

On the main menu of the Data View, choose Analyze / Descriptive Statistics / Frequencies.

Select the variable(s) you wish to analyze, in this case the numerical life expectancy. Click on the arrow to move life expectancy into the variable list. Now select the Statistics... button on the right. By checking off the appropriate boxes we can calculate all the desired statistics: Mean, Median, Mode, Std deviation, Range, Minimum and Maximum. We can also check off the Quartiles box (or any other partition of the data into any number of cuts). Press the Continue button.

Now choose the Charts... button on the Frequencies dialog box. Choose Histograms and Continue. We are now ready to generate all results by pressing the OK button.

The output screen will contain:

Statistics		
Numeric Value		
N	Valid	194
	Missing	0
Mean		70.01
Median		72.50
Mode		74
Std. Deviation		9.259
Range		36
Minimum		47
5Maximum		83
Percentiles	25	63.75
	50	72.50
	75	76.25

Figure 5.5

And

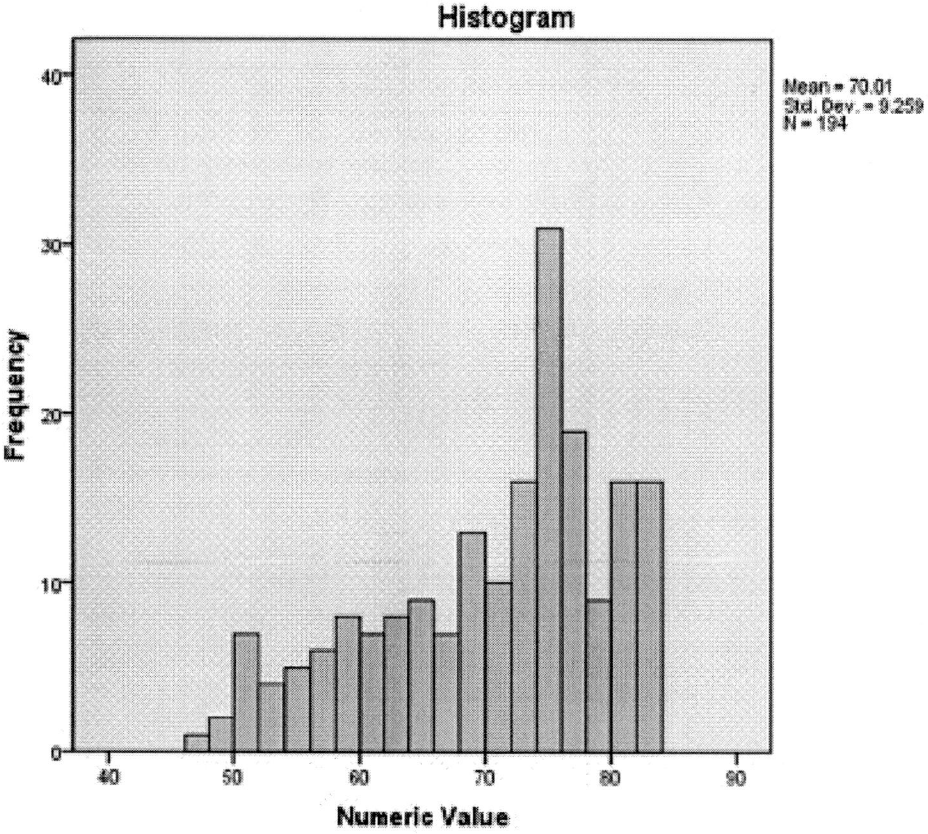

Figure 5.6

SPSS has automatically chosen the widths and number of bins to use for the histogram but we can edit the result to use the same categories as we used in Excel.

Double clicking on the histogram will activate the Chart Editor. You can make numerous adjustments to the histogram such as changing color, fonts and bin size to name a few.

In the Chart Editor window double click on a histogram bar to open the Properties dialog box. You can also access the Properties box via the Chart Editor Edit menu but you must click on the histogram first. Choose the Binning tab and click on the Custom option for the X axis. Enter the number 6 for the Interval width and check the box for Custom value for anchor. Enter the value 46 to match the starting value used in Excel. Click on the Apply button to complete the changes to the histogram.

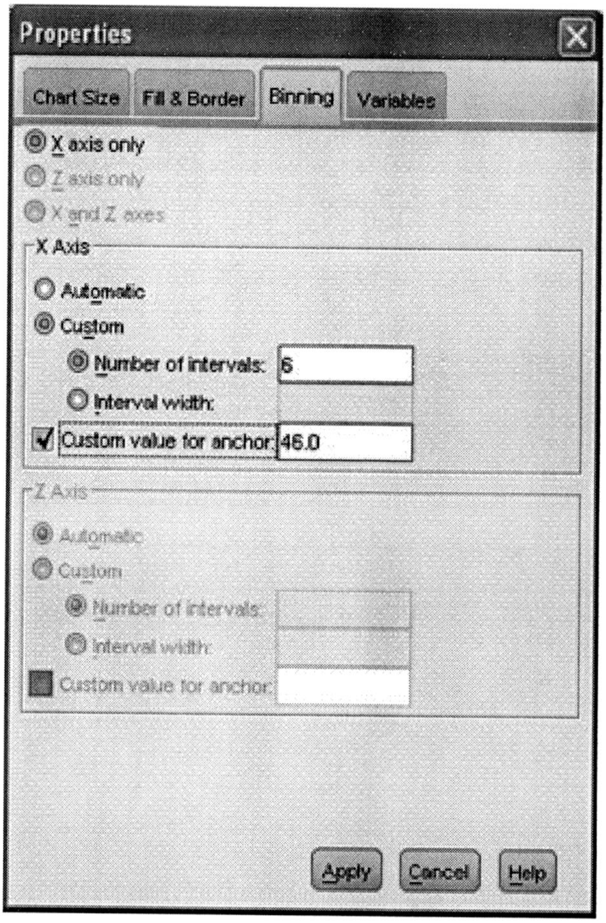

Figure 5.7

We can also add data labels to the SPSS graph to verify that it is using the same frequency values as Excel. In the Chart Editor choose the Elements menu and click on the Show Data Labels option.

The final result is shown below. The SPSS graph is a true histogram since the bars of the chart are contiguous. You can verify that the values on each bar do indeed match the interval values calculated in Excel.

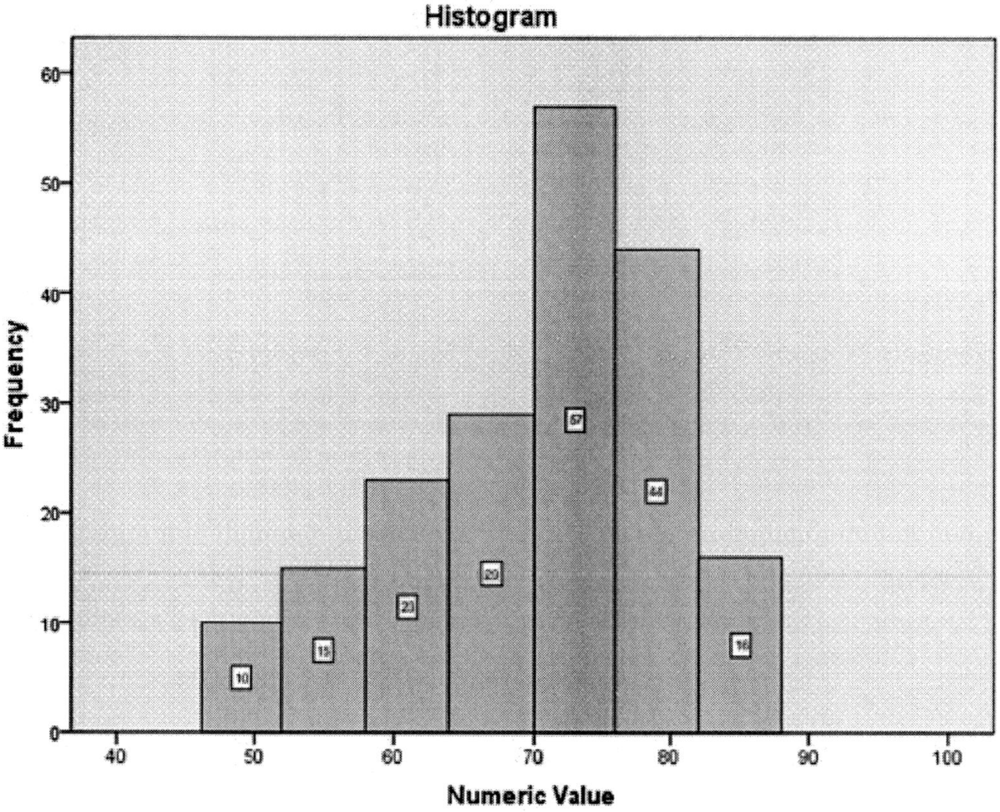

Figure 5.8

You can see that SPSS gives very nicely formatted results with minimal effort. Before we end the discussion let's revisit the topic of filtering data.

Having looked at the results so far, we decide that we'd like to limit our analysis to just countries in Europe, or just countries in Africa. Return to the Data Editor Screen and on the main menu line, choose Data. Choose the next to last entry in the list, Select Cases... to open the dialog box. Choose the "If condition is satisfied" option, then press the If... button. Now select the variable WHOregion and press the arrow to move it to the formula editor. Add the phrase = "Europe" in the editor as shown below. Note that you must enclose the name of the region in quotes since it is a string value.

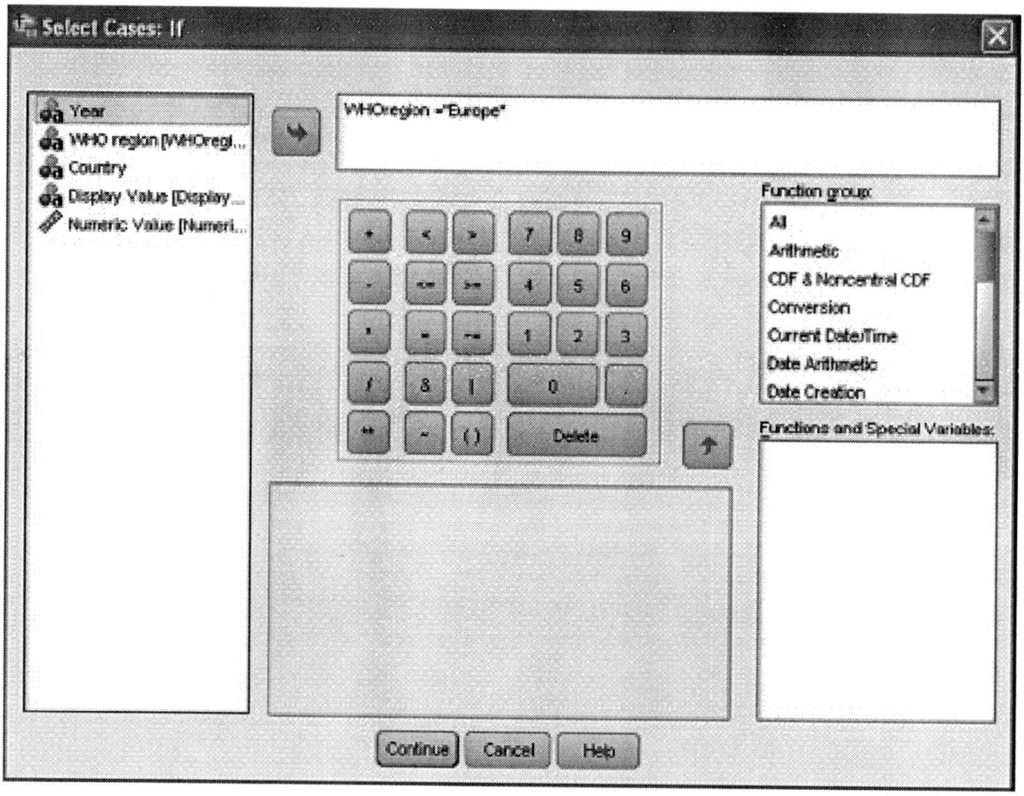

Figure 5.9

Press Continue to return to the Select Cases dialog box. In the Output section you have options about how to treat the filtered data. To just view it temporarily use the first choice. You should rarely use the last choice (Delete unselected cases) since that will result in the permanent loss of data. Using the **Filter out unselected cases** option, press OK. Return once again to the Data View of the Data Editor screen. All non-European countries are "crossed out" but remain part of the data set. Recalculate the statistics and histogram for the filtered set. The results screen now shows the values and histogram for the 53 European countries only.

It is worth noting that to achieve the same result in Excel you would have to use some form of =IF formulas to get the correct results. The filtering mechanism in Excel changes the view only. The data remains active in the background.

EXERCISES

In the study cited in Chapter 2 Exercise 1, the diameter of each plant within the plot was measured. The following table shows the measurements of the diameters of each plant in a particular plot (used with permission, Dr. Lance Evans, Biology Department, Manhattan College, Riverdale, NY).

Plant	Diameter (m)	Plant	Diameter (m)	Plant	Diameter (m)
PO	0.9	P12	0.85	P24	1
P1	1.7	P13	2.4	P25	0.7
P2	1.7	P14	0.7	P26	1.4
P3	2	P15	1.1	P27	0.8
P4	1	P16	0.1	P28	1.8
P5	1.9	P17	1.1	P29	0.6
P6	1.3	P18	0.5	P30	0.5
P7	1.1	P19	0.55	P31	0.9
P8	0.7	P20	0.9	P32	1.8
P9	1.5	P21	1.1	P33	0.2
P10	0.6	P22	1	P34	0.4
P11	0.6	P23	0.6		

Using both the spreadsheet method and SPSS:

1. Find the summary statistics: mean, median, mode, standard deviation, minimum, maximum and range
2. Create the frequency table and histogram (suggestion: use 5 bins).

Probability Distributions

Let's consider our analysis of life expectancy from a different perspective. Suppose that instead of just counting how many nations fall into each class interval, we want to know what percentage of nations fall into that interval. In other words, we can present our data as a comparison of the number of countries in any class interval with the total number of countries represented in the study. We would create a ratio of class size/ total. This ratio is referred to as the Relative Frequency.

The histograms for frequency and relative frequency have the exact same shape. The only thing that changes is the scale of the vertical axis. In our life expectancy example there are 10/194 (or 5/97) countries that have a life expectancy in the interval from 46 to 51. The possible frequency values go from 10 to the maximum of 57, the relative frequency values go from 10/194 to 57 /194.

Look again at the frequency table. A column is now added for all the relative frequencies. This quantity can also be thought of as the likelihood or probability of randomly choosing a country from our sample that is in a particular interval. In general a probability is a measure of the ratio of the number of ways a desired event occurs/the total number of ways the event may occur, often represented as a decimal value. Multiplying the values in the probability column by 100 yields the percentages in column L.

	G	H	I	J	K	L
15	INTERVALS	BINS	FREQUENCY	RELATIVE FREQUENCY	PROBABILITY	PERCENT
16	46-51	51	10	5/97	0.052	5.2%
17	52-57	57	15	15/194	0.077	7.7%
18	58-63	63	23	23/194	0.119	11.9%
19	64-69	69	29	29/194	0.149	14.9%
20	70-75	75	57	57/194	0.294	29.4%
21	76-81	81	44	22/97	0.227	22.7%
22	82-87	87	16	8/97	0.082	8.2%
23	Total:		194	194/194	1.000	100%

Table 6.1

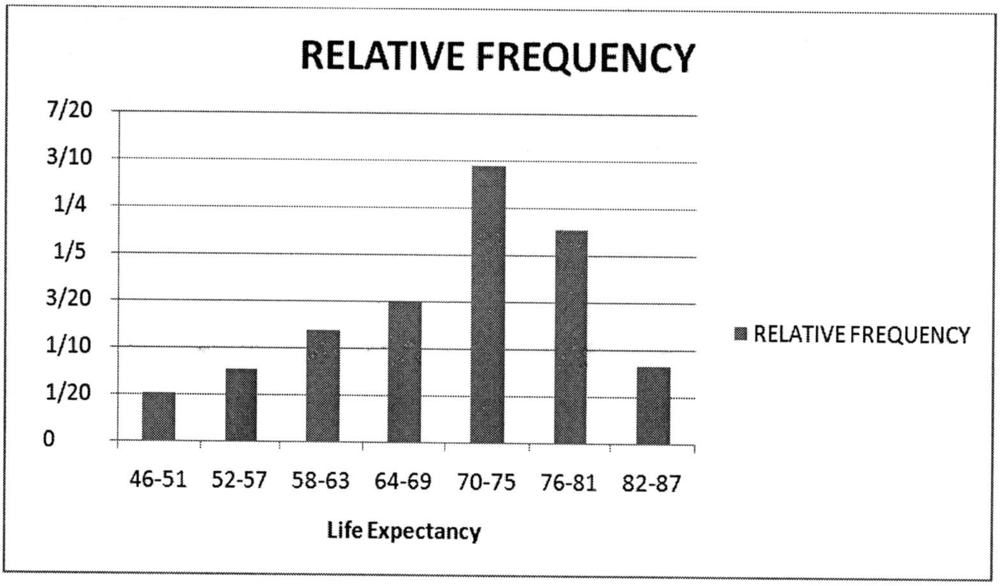

Figure 6.1

Note that for all probabilities, designated as P(X), $0 \leq P(X) \leq 1$ where a probability of 0 indicates that the event is impossible, and a probability of 1 indicates that the event must occur or is certain.

Since we are interested in how many ways events can occur, it is helpful to have some tools for counting. The fundamental principal of counting says that for a sequence of two events, if event1 can occur in n_1 ways and event2 can occur in n_2 ways, then the number of ways in which both the first and second event can occur is $n_1 \cdot n_2$.

This principal can be expanded to look at the number of ways events or items can be arranged or grouped. If you wish to determine the number of ways n objects can be arranged, the possibilities would be calculated as $n \cdot (n-1) \cdot (n-2) \cdot \ldots \cdot 1$ or **n factorial**. If only r of the n objects are arranged in a particular order, we are talking about a **Permutation** of the items. Lastly, if we want to know the number of ways in which items can be grouped, we are talking about a **Combination** of those items.

Below is a list of the mathematical symbol, definition and Excel equivalent for each technique. Let n denote the size of the pool of candidates from which to make our selection and r represents the number of "items" we are choosing at any given time.

Name	Symbol	Formula	Excel
Factorial	n!	$n \cdot (n-1) \cdot (n-2) \cdot \ldots \cdot 1$	=FACT(n)
Permutation	nPr	$\frac{n!}{(n-r)!}$	=PERMUT(n, r)
Combination	nCr	$\frac{n!}{r!(n-r)!}$	=COMBIN(n, r)

Table 6.2

So if we have 10 volunteers for an experiment and we want to create teams of 4, we will have a combination of 10 volunteers taken 4 at a time, nCr =COMBIN(n, r). There are ${}_{10}C_4 = 120$ different teams that can be chosen from the pool of candidates.

If the team members have a rank: the first person is the leader, the second is the assistant, the third is the recorder, and the fourth is the presenter, then we have a permutation of 10 volunteers taken 4 at a time, nPr =PERMUT(n, r). There are ${}_{10}P_4 = 5040$ possible arrangements of those same candidates!

MULTIPLICATION/ADDITION RULES

We often look at the probability of some series of outcomes or a subset of possible outcomes. A general rule of thumb for counting is that the word AND is translated as multiplication, while the word OR is translated as addition.

For independent events the probability that two outcomes both happen is given by the rule

$$P(A \text{ and } B) = P(A) \cdot P(B).$$

For example, if a couple has 3 children, the probability that all three are boys would be the probability that the first is a boy AND the second is a boy AND the third is a boy or $\frac{1}{2} \cdot \frac{1}{2} \cdot \frac{1}{2} = 1/8$.

If we choose a country at random from our life expectancy study, the probability that the life expectancy is one of the extreme values, that is, $P(X \leq 51 \text{ or } X \geq 82) = 0.052 + 0.082 = 0.134$.

In general, if the outcomes are mutually exclusive (no possibility of overlap) then

$$P(A \text{ or } B) = P(A) + P(B).$$

If there is an overlap between the outcomes then we must make sure that the overlapping area is only counted once, or $P(A \text{ or } B) = P(A) + P(B) - P(A \text{ and } B)$

Another useful notion for calculating probability is that of the **complement** of an event. If we divide the possible outcomes of an event into 2 subsets: S1= those that are desired and S2 = all the rest of the possibilities, then S1 and S2 are called complements and P(S1) + P(S2) = 1, which gives us an alternative way to calculate P(S1): **P(S1) = 1 – P(S2).**

Sometimes a probability is easier to calculate by "coming in the back door." For example, if we wanted to know the probability of choosing a country from our study where the life expectancy is greater than 51 we could add all the probabilities from the second interval to the last interval, $P(52 \leq X \leq 57) + P(58 \leq X \leq 63) + \ldots + P(82 \leq X \leq 87)$

Or we could recognize that the complement of "life expectancy is greater than 51" is "life expectancy is NOT greater than 51" which in this study, is the interval 46–51. So

P(life expectancy is greater than 51) = $1 - P(46 \leq X \leq 51) = 1 - 0.052 = 0.948$.

RANDOM VARIABLES AND DISCRETE DISTRIBUTIONS

Suppose we can describe some event, call it X so we don't have to keep writing whole phrases. And further suppose that X has distinct numerical possible outcomes such as 1, 2, 3, 4, 5. Then X is called a **discrete random variable**. We can construct a probability table for X that contains all possible outcomes of the event, a legitimate probability measure for each outcome ($0 \leq P(X) \leq 1$) and we require that the sum of all the probabilities must equal 1. This probability table is known as a **probability distribution** for the random variable X.

Let's take a closer look at these concepts by collecting some information about World Series baseball games. From 1903 to 2012 there have been 105 "best of 7 games" World Series. http://www.baseball-almanac.com/ws/wsmenu.shtm

(Periodically there has been an attempt to play a best of 9 games series, usually to increase revenue.)

If we let the variable X represent the number of games played in the World Series, X can have 4 possible values ranging from 4 to 7. Since the value of X can vary and take on a finite number of values, it is a discrete random variable. We can construct the relative frequency table for the number of games played using historical data.

Number of Games	Frequency	Relative Frequency
4	21	21/105
5	24	24/105
6	23	23/105
7	37	37/105
Total	105	105/105

Table 6.3

We are now ready to give a more formal statement of our study.

Let X= the number of games played in the World Series.

x is a particular value from 4 to 7.

$P(X=x)$ is the probability that exactly x games will be played to complete the World Series.

Using the historical relative frequency we can approximate the discrete probability distribution for the number of World Series games played. Recall that the command = ROUND(value, places) can be used to round off the probability values typically to 3 places after the decimal.

We verify that this is a true distribution by noting that all possible outcomes are included, each probability measure is between 0 and 1 and the sum of the probabilities = 1.

	A	B
1	X	P(X)
2	4	0.200
3	5	0.229
4	6	0.219
5	7	0.352
6	Total	1.000

Table 6.4

When we have a probability distribution we can calculate the "expected value" of the event as

$$\textbf{(6.1)} \qquad \text{E[X]} = \sum_{i=1n}^{n} x_i P(X = x_i)$$

So the expected number of games for a World Series is

$$4(0.200) + 5(0.229) + 6(0.219) + 7(0.352) = 5.724 \text{ or } \sim 6 \text{ games.}$$

This value is a weighted average and can be calculated in Excel using the formula

= SUMPRODUCT(A2:A5, B2:B5).

Note that the arrays (A2:A5, B2:B5) must be the same size and in the same direction, that is both are arranged in columns or both are arranged in rows.

CUMULATIVE DISTRIBUTIONS

For each probability distribution we can create an on-going sum called the **cumulative distribution.** This is simply the sum of all probabilities up to and including the particular value of the random variable under consideration. The first entry is the same as the probability of the first outcome, the last entry is always 1.

	A	B	C	
1	X	P(X)	P(X≤ x)	
2	4	0.200	0.200	
3	5	0.229	0.429	← = B3 + C2
4	6	0.219	0.648	← = B4 + C3
5	7	0.352	1.000	
6	Total	1.000		

Table 6.5

We have seen that probabilities can be represented as ratios, decimals and percentages. We can also think of probability as a measure of AREA. If you consider each bar of the histogram as a rectangle whose width is 1 and whose height is equal to the probability for that value of X then

$$\text{Area(rectangle)} = \text{width} \cdot \text{height} = 1 \cdot P(X=x) = P(X=x).$$

The cumulative probability is the sum of the areas of the rectangles up to and including the particular rectangle under consideration. The image of probability as area will become more significant as we consider some special distributions in the following sections.

BINOMIAL DISTRIBUTION

We define a **binomial distribution** to be an experiment in which

- there are a fixed number of independent trials (the outcome of any trial is not affected by earlier outcomes),
- each trial has only 2 possible outcomes we refer to as success (that is the item we are counting) or failure (the alternative outcome) and
- the probability of each outcome remains the same throughout the course of the experiment.

A classic example of a binomial distribution is one that counts the number of heads that occur when a coin is flipped a specified number of times or the number of male births in an n-child family. These two cases happen to also represent **equally likely events.** We expect a coin to show "heads" half the time. Similarly, when considering the birth of a child, the probability of a boy being born is ½.

Below is a representation, called a **tree diagram,** of ALL possible gender outcomes for "an experiment" in which a family has three children.

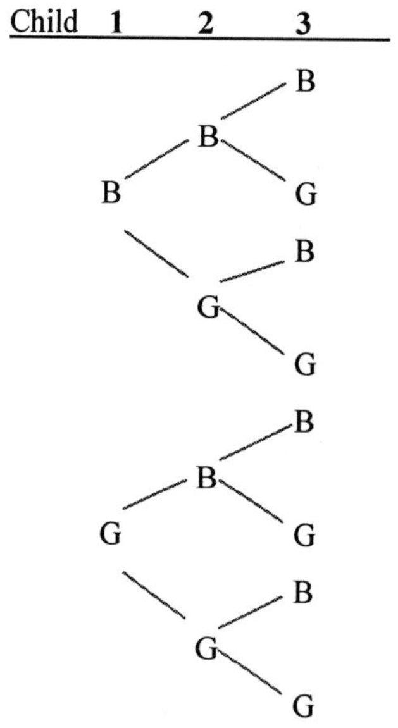

Figure 6.2

An alternate representation of the 8 possible configurations corresponding to each path above is given by the following list called a **sample space:** (B, B, B), (B, B, G), (B, G, B), (B,G,G),(G, B, B), (G, B, G), (G,G, B), (G,G,G). Each triple in the space represents an implicit AND statement. P (B, G, B) represents the probability of a boy **and** a girl **and** a boy. So the probability for each path is ½ · ½ · ½ = 1/8.

So in calculating the probability for each value of x, the question to ask is "In how many paths are there *x* Girls?" We don't care what the order is, just how many possibilities exist. There are 3 paths that have exactly 1 girl so the probability that a family will have exactly 1 girl is

(6.2) $P(X=1) = 3 \cdot ½ \cdot ½ \cdot ½ = 3/8.$

Recall that a short cut way to answer the question of "how many ways can I pick x number of girls from a pool of 3 children?" is to use the combination of ${}_3C_x$. If we let p represent the probability of "success", the birth of a girl, and q=1–p, the probability of "failure", the birth of a boy, then equation (6.2) can be written as

(6.3) $P(X=1) = {}_3C_1 \cdot p \cdot q \cdot q = {}_3C_1 \cdot p^1 \cdot q^2$

In general the binomial probability for x successes in n trials is

(6.4) $P(X=x) = {}_nC_x \cdot p^x \cdot q^{n-x}$

The Excel commands for each of the distributions we will study follow the same general pattern. The most notable parameter is the last one. The same command is used to calculate both the distribution and the cumulative distribution. The last parameter in the command lets you specify which one you want: FALSE for the probability distribution and TRUE for the cumulative probability distribution.

The Excel command for the binomial distribution is

= BINOM.DIST (number of successes, number of trials, probability of success, cumulative distribution)

Using the notation in the chart below this would be =BINOM.DIST(x col values, n, p, FALSE)

The complete distribution and cumulative distribution for the above experiment is

	A	B	C
1	X: the number of girls		
2	n =	3	
3	p =	0.5	
4	q =	0.5	
5			
6	X	P(X)	P(X≤ x)
7	0	0.125	0.125
8	1	0.375	0.500
9	2	0.375	0.875
10	3	0.125	1.000

Table 6.6

Showing the formulas:

X: the number of girls		
n =	3	
p =	0.5	
q =	0.5	
X	P(X)	P(X≤ x)
0	=BINOM.DIST(A7,$B$2,$B$3,FALSE)	=BINOM.DIST(A7,$B$2,$B$3,TRUE)
1	=BINOM.DIST(A8,$B$2,$B$3,FALSE)	=BINOM.DIST(A8,$B$2,$B$3,TRUE)
2	=BINOM.DIST(A9,$B$2,$B$3,FALSE)	=BINOM.DIST(A9,$B$2,$B$3,TRUE)
3	=BINOM.DIST(A10,$B$2,$B$3,FALSE)	=BINOM.DIST(A10,$B$2,$B$3,TRUE)

Table 6.7

The probability distribution graphs:

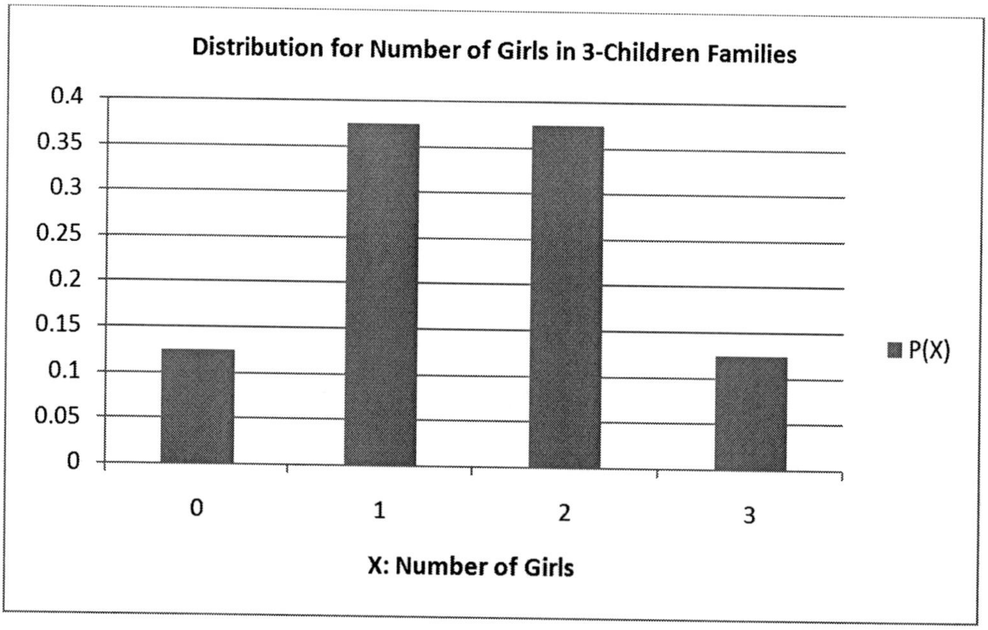

Figure 6.3

Note that the only parameter values needed to determine the binomial distribution are the number of trials, n and the probability of success p. The expected value or mean of the binomial random variable can be found by the expected value formula (6.1), but for the binomial this simplifies to $E[X]= n{\cdot}p$ and the standard deviation is $\sqrt{n \cdot p \cdot q \cdot}$.

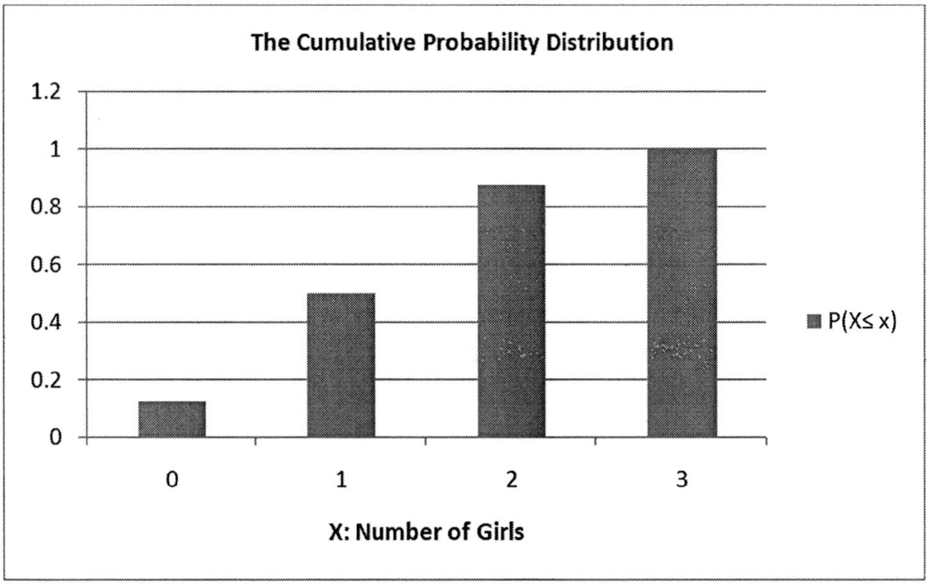

Figure 6.4

POISSON DISTRIBUTION

The Poisson Distribution is another countable (discrete) distribution. However, unlike the binomial distribution, there may be more than two outcomes, in fact the number of outcomes is theoretically limitless. We usually define the experiment to be within a certain time period or a context (the number of typographical errors on a page). In the example below the number of babies born in a night is the event under consideration. The probability of a Poisson random variable is calculated using the negative exponential function and a single parameter, the mean, which is represented by the Greek letter lambda, λ. You may have noticed that mathematicians think it is cool to use Greek letters in their equations.

The added bonus of the Poisson distribution is that the expected value is known at the start (λ) and the standard deviation is $\sqrt{\lambda}$. We can also use the Poisson to approximate the binomial probability by using $\lambda = n{\cdot}p$ when there are many trials and the probability of "success" is small. Think creatively here: if you are modeling disease 'the probability of "success" is small' may be interpreted as 'the number of mutant cells in a culture (success) is much smaller than the number of healthy cells (failure).' The Poisson probability is given by

(6.5) $P(X=x) = e^{-\lambda}\lambda^{x}/x!$

Excel uses the formulas $P(X= x)$: = POISSON.DIST(*x value*,λ,*FALSE*)

And $P(X\leq x)$: = POISSON.DIST(*x value*,λ,*TRUE*)

The following example is taken from the Mathematical Association (UK) document "REAL LIFE EXAMPLES IN MEDICAL STATISTICS"

(http://www.m-a.org.uk/jsp/index.jsp?lnk=421#RealLifeExamplesInMedicalStatistics).

Here's an example where the Poisson distribution was used in a maternity hospital to work out how many births would be expected during the night.

The hospital had 3000 deliveries each year, so if these happened randomly around the clock 1000 deliveries would be expected between the hours of midnight and 8.00 a.m. This is the time when many staff are off duty and it is important to ensure that there will be enough people to cope with the workload on any particular night.

The average number of deliveries per night is 1000/365, which is 2.74. From this average rate the probability of delivering 0,1,2, etc. babies each night can be calculated using the Poisson distribution.

The Poisson distributions and their graphs are:

	A	B	C
1	X: the # of babies born in 1 night		
2	Lambda =	2.74	
3	X	P(X = x)	P(X ≤ x)
4	0	0.065	0.065
5	1	0.177	0.241
6	2	0.242	0.484
7	3	0.221	0.705
8	4	0.152	0.857
9	5	0.083	0.940
10	6	0.038	0.978
11	7	0.015	0.993
12	8	0.005	0.998
13	9	0.002	0.999
14	10	0.000	1.000

Table 6.8

	A	B	C
	X: the # of babies born in 1 night		
1	Lambda =	2.74	
2	X	P(X = x)	P(X ≤ x)
3	0	=POISSON.DIST(A4,$B$2,FALSE)	=POISSON.DIST(A4,$B$2,TRUE)
4	1	=POISSON.DIST(A5,$B$2,FALSE)	=POISSON.DIST(A5,$B$2,TRUE)
5	2	=POISSON.DIST(A6,$B$2,FALSE)	=POISSON.DIST(A6,$B$2,TRUE)
6	3	=POISSON.DIST(A7,$B$2,FALSE)	=POISSON.DIST(A7,$B$2,TRUE)
7	4	=POISSON.DIST(A8,$B$2,FALSE)	=POISSON.DIST(A8,$B$2,TRUE)
8	5	=POISSON.DIST(A9,$B$2,FALSE)	=POISSON.DIST(A9,$B$2,TRUE)
9	6	=POISSON.DIST(A10,$B$2,FALSE)	=POISSON.DIST(A10,$B$2,TRUE)
10	7	=POISSON.DIST(A11,$B$2,FALSE)	=POISSON.DIST(A11,$B$2,TRUE)
11	8	=POISSON.DIST(A12,$B$2,FALSE)	=POISSON.DIST(A12,$B$2,TRUE)
12	9	=POISSON.DIST(A13,$B$2,FALSE)	=POISSON.DIST(A13,$B$2,TRUE)
13	10	=POISSON.DIST(A14,$B$2,FALSE)	=POISSON.DIST(A14,$B$2,TRUE)

Table 6.9

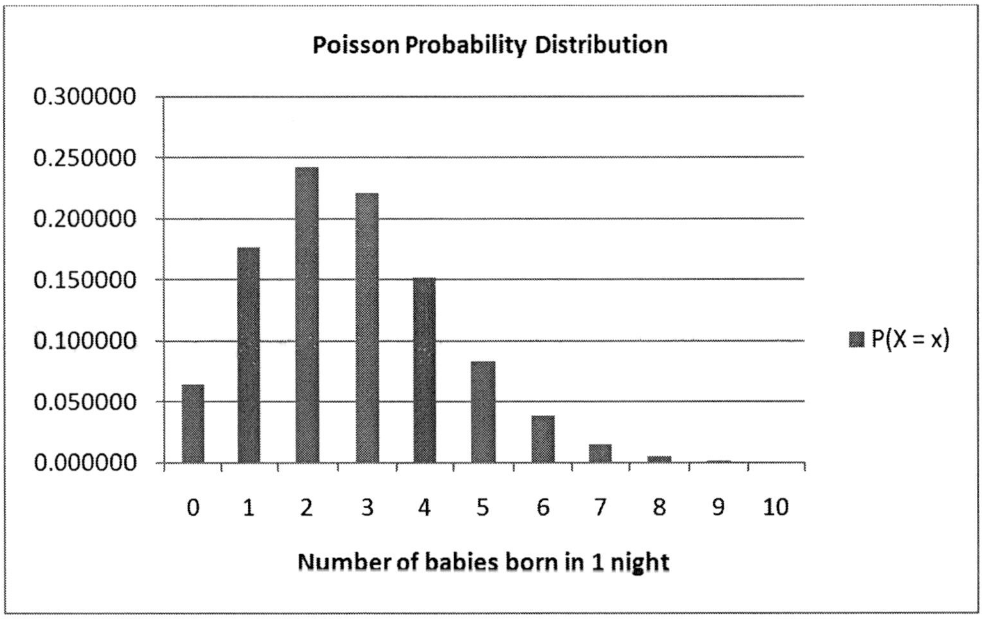

Figure 6.5

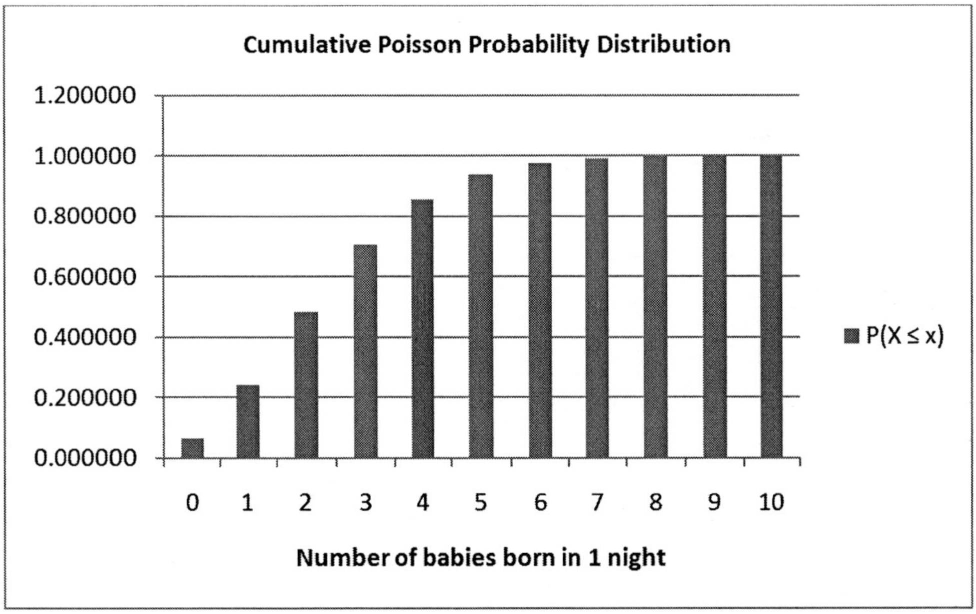

Figure 6.6

Since the Poisson distribution has the possibility of an infinite number of outcomes, a question to ask is "when do we stop?" Take a close look at row 14 of the table 6.10. The probability values have been rounded to 3 places, so it appears that the possibility of 10 births in a given night is 0. However, the $P(X=10) = 0.000424$ and $P(X \leq 10) = 0.999864$. So 10 (or more) births in one night is a POSSIBLE event, but it is highly unlikely. It is reasonable to stop calculating the distribution when the probability of the outcome gets close to 0. Figure 6.5 suggests that 8 would be the maximum likely number of births. Note also that the distribution should be approximately centered around the mean. In this case the mean is almost 3 ($\lambda = 2.74$), so it is reasonable to expect the bulk of the distribution to be between 0 and 6. Extend your chart a little further to give a more robust representation. It is important to remember that although the Poisson random variable can increase without bound, the total probability, or total area of the graph, must equal 1.

We can use the probabilities calculated in table 6.10 to estimate the busyness of the delivery room. For example, the probability that there will be at least 4 births in 1 night is

$$P(X \geq 4) = 1 - P(X < 4) = 1 - P(X \leq 3) = 1 - 0.705 = 0.295.$$

The number of days in which we expect this to happen is 365*0.295 or approximately 108 days.

FROM BINOMIAL TO NORMAL

Let's return for a moment to the simplest binomial experiment, any event with 2 equally likely outcomes such as flipping a coin. Clearly, if we could spend a day flipping a coin, each flip would be independent of the one before it, and we could conduct this "experiment" a very large number of times, so we have a large n number of independent trials with the probability of each outcome = ½.

If we construct several probability distributions to count the number of heads, the distribution of outcomes for 2 flips would be as shown in figure 6.7 and 3 flips would be identical to those created for the case of counting the number of girls in a family of 3 children given in figure 6.3.

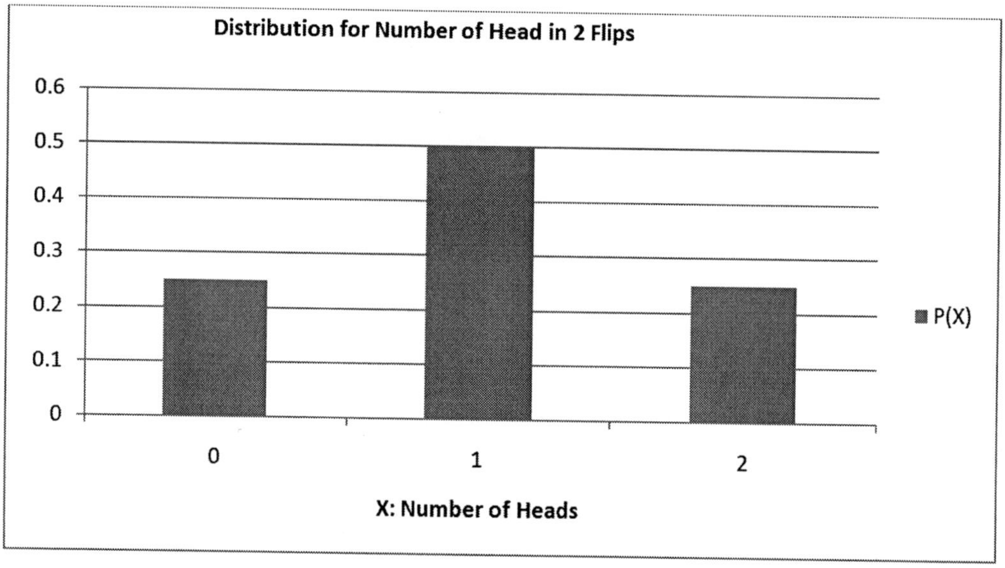

Figure 6.7

If we flip the coin 8 times and count the number of heads the probability distribution for the event would be:

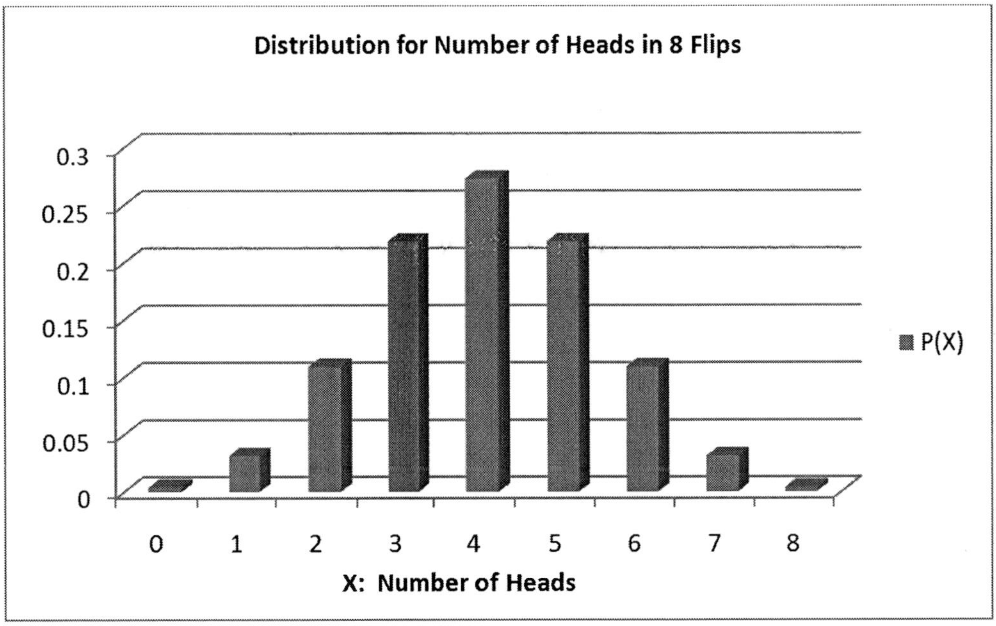

Figure 6.8

Similarly, 10 flips of the coin would yield:

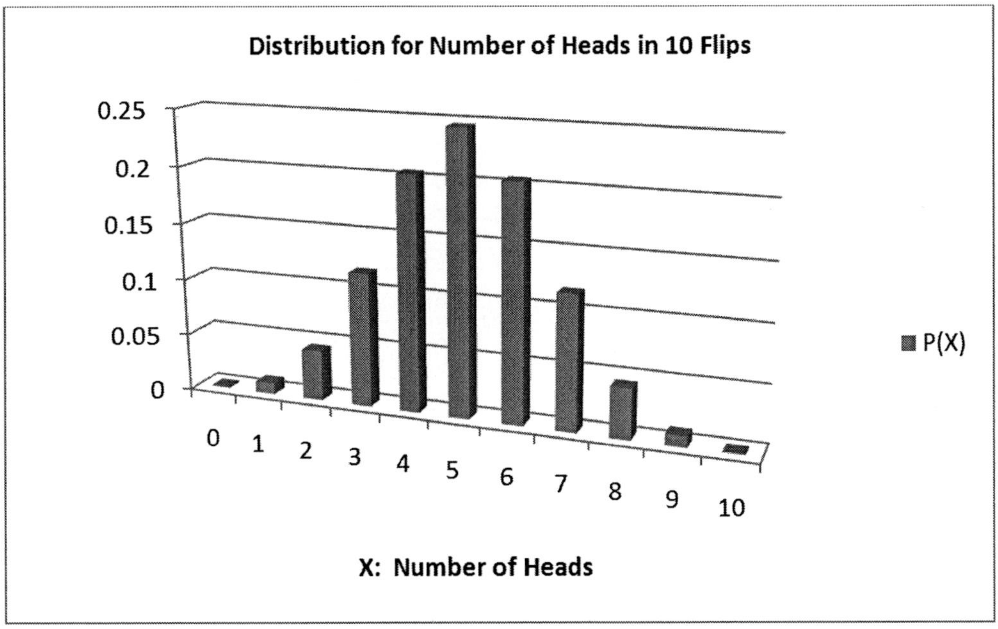

Figure 6.9

The basic idea is to recognize that the larger n is, the more the histogram looks like a bell-shaped curve which is associated with the Normal Distribution. We will return to the relationship of the binomial to the normal, but first let's consider the Normal Distribution itself.

NORMAL DISTRIBUTION

So far we have considered discrete random variables. In each distribution, X took on distinct, exact values. However, if the values of X extend over an **interval** then X is called a **continuous random variable**. There is little doubt that the most important continuous probability distribution is the Normal Distribution. Not only does the normal distribution occur naturally, such as in IQ testing, it can also be shown mathematically that if you take samples of size n from <u>any</u> probability distribution and find the mean of the scores chosen, the distribution of all such sample means will approach a normal distribution. This phenomenon is referred to as the Central Limit Theorem. As a result the Normal is the "goto" distribution for most statistical studies, especially when one is trying to verify certain hypotheses about how closely a particular sample represents a population.

The normal distribution has the following properties:

- The parameters used to describe the normal curve are its mean <u>mu</u> (μ) and its standard deviation <u>sigma</u> (σ). More Greek! Note that μ will determine the height of the curve and σ its width or dispersion.
- The total area under the bell curve is equal to 1. This is analogous to the sum of the areas of the bars in the discrete distribution.
- The distribution (and its curve) is completely symmetrical about the mean, and the mean equals the median and the mode.
- Approximately 68% of the X values will fall between the mean and plus or minus 1 standard deviation; approximately 95% of the values will fall between the mean and plus or minus 2 standard deviations; approximately 99.7% of the values will fall between the mean and plus or minus 3 standard deviations.

Excel provides the following usual functions for the probability and cumulative probability. The cumulative distribution command is:

$P(X \leq x)$ = NORM.DIST(x value, μ, σ, TRUE)

However, there is an important distinction between the commands for the continuous random variables and those of the previous discrete random variables when using the above command with the FALSE parameter. It is imperative to realize that the distribution command =NORM.DIST(x, μ, σ, **FALSE**) **does not** produce a probability measure. It is referred to as the probability **density** function *f(x)* and is the y-value or height of the curve. You can use this to draw a smooth curve scatter diagram of the bell curve.

The Normal distribution, like the Poisson is defined using a negative exponential function. The value of the density function is calculated by

(6.6) $$f(x)=\frac{1}{\sqrt{2\pi}\sigma}e^{-(x-\mu)^2/2\sigma^2}$$

The command = NORM.DIST(x value, μ, σ, FALSE) is used ONLY to draw the graph of the function. ALL probability values should be obtained by utilizing the cumulative distribution, that is, use the **TRUE** option in the NORM.DIST function. The probabilities are obtained by slicing the curve into the desired pieces, knowing that the total area is 1 and the calculated area from the NORM.DIST function is everything from the far left up to the number given.

So, for example, to find the probability that X is in the interval (x_1, x_2) use

$$P(x_1 \le X \le x_2) = P(X \le x_2) - P(X \le x_1)$$

As an illustration, suppose the Park's Department runs a fitness program for young children. The age of children who participate is normally distributed with a mean of 5 and a standard deviation of 0.5. The normal distribution is written as N(μ, σ). In this case we have the ages of the children distributed as N(5, 0.5).

To create the bell curve for this scenario, recall that 99.7% of the children's ages will be within 3 standard deviations of the mean. In other words, almost all the children are between 5− 3(0.5) and 5 + 3(0.5) or, the ages are in the interval (3.5, 6.5). It is always possible for a child younger or older than this range to show up, but it is very unlikely. So when drawing the graph use a slightly larger domain, say from 3.0 to 7.0.

	A	B	C
	X: age of children participating in Parks Dpt.		
1	Program		
2	mu =	5	
3	sigma =	0.5	
4			
5	X	f(x)	P(X≤x)
6	3	0.000	0.000
7	3.5	0.009	0.001
8	4	0.108	0.023
9	4.5	0.484	0.159
10	5	0.798	0.500
11	5.5	0.484	0.841
12	6	0.108	0.977
13	6.5	0.009	0.999
14	7	0.000	1.000

Table 6.10

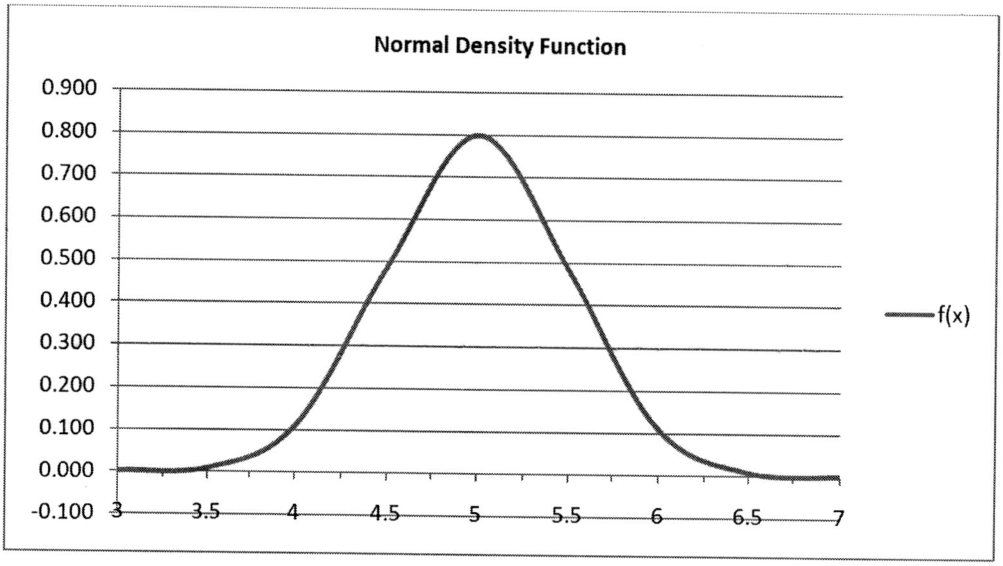

Figure 6.10

Note that, as we had seen with the Poisson distribution, $P(X \le x)$ at the values of 3 and 7 are not actually 0 and 1 but very close to those numbers. Rounding the probabilities to 3 decimals gives the illusion that the curve actually meets the x-axis. This never actually happens – there's always the possibility of another score to the left or right. But the question to ask your self is "does it make any sense to consider scores that are higher or lower than the defined space under consideration?" If the answer is no, then the set-up is sufficient. If the answer is yes, you may need to adjust your table.

Note on the table that when $X = 5$, $P(X \le x)$ is 0.500. The mean always splits the curve in half – the curve is said to be symmetric about the mean. Half the area will always be to the left of the mean, and half the area will be to the right of the mean.

There is no EXACT single value to be calculated in the Normal Distribution (try to draw a rectangle under a single point on the curve to calculate area).

So $P(x_1 \le X \le x_2) = P(x_1 < X < x_2)$.

Below are some sample probability calculations for the Parks Department program using Table 6.12.

1. Between two numbers

   $P(4.5 < X < 5.0)$

   $= P(X < 5.0) - P(X < 4.5)$

   = C10 – C9

   =0.500 – 0.159

   =0.341

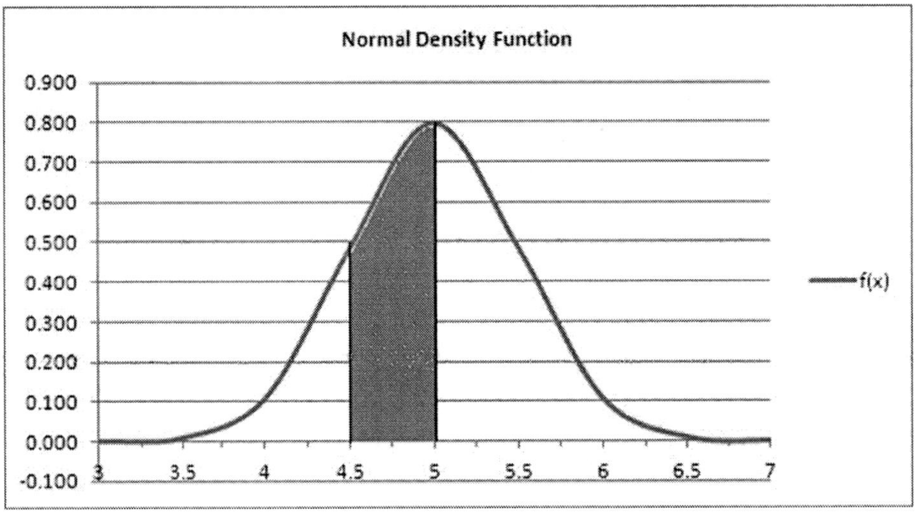

Figure 6.11

2. Left Tail
   P(X < 4)
   = C8
   = 0.023

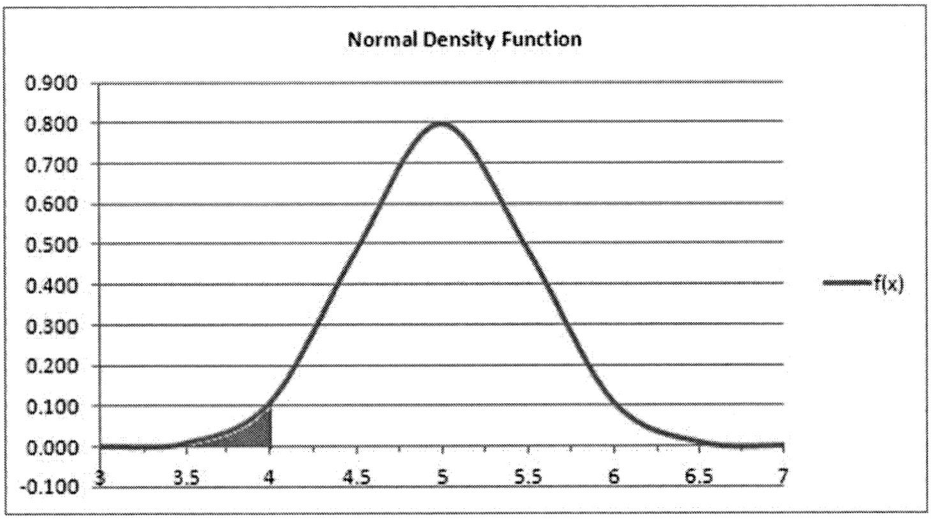

Figure 6.12

3. Right Tail
   P(X > 5.5)
   = 1 – P(X < 5.5)
   = 1 – C11
   = 1 – 0.841
   = 0.159

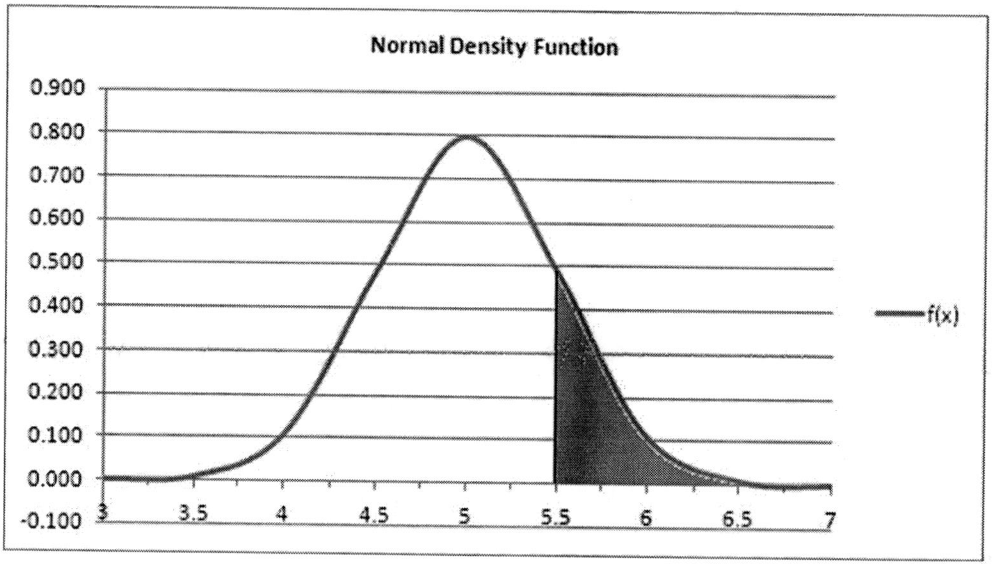

Figure 6. 13

For values of X that are not listed in your graph (4.25, for example), either insert the value into the table or use it directly in the Norm.Dist formula.

It is possible to use the normal distribution to approximate values of the binomial distribution by allowing $\mu = n{\cdot}p$, and $\sigma = \sqrt{n \cdot p \cdot q \cdot}$. However since the normal is a continuous random variable, a slight correction is needed to capture the exact value of the binomial. If in the binomial we want to know P(X = 90) we should use the interval (89.5, 90.5) in the normal distribution. This will approximately be the same area as a 1 unit wide rectangle with a height that corresponds to P(X = 90). It would be a very tedious process to calculate P(X≤ 90) by hand (the sum of all probabilities up to and including P(X = 90)). But the benefit of using a normal approximation of P(X≤ 90.5) for such a calculation is greatly lessened by the use of computers and calculators.

Excel provides an additional formula for the normal distribution that allows us to reverse the process we've been using so far. We have been looking for the probabilities associated with given values of the random variable regardless of the type of distribution under consideration.

For the Normal Distribution we have the ability to say "what is the value of X associated with a given probability measure for this distribution." We might have information about the percentage covered in a normal distribution but not have the scores that are associated with that percentage or probability.

The NORM.INV formula returns the inverse of this probability, that is, it changes the cumulative probability into an actual number (X) from the distribution. Suppose the Parks Department staff wants to create a special activity for the older children. They have determined that they have room for about 15% of the children for this activity. What should be the cut-off age for the new program?

We can use the command = NORM.INV(probability, μ, σ) to find the value of the random variable X associated with the stated probability. In this case we are looking at the right tail for the upper 15% which is equivalent to 85% from the left, so we can use

X = NORM.INV(0.850, 5,0.5) = 5.5.

The new program should be made available to children who are 5½ and older.

We can use the NORM.INV function to create a simulation of an experiment by randomly generating probability values using the RAND( ) function. RAND( ) generates random numbers between 0 and 1 – which is exactly the range of values for probability measures. So we can imbed the RAND( ) command inside the NORM. INV command:

(6.7) = NORM.INV(RAND( ), μ, σ)

This command will generate random values that simulate, for example, the heights of players on the college basketball team, given a particular mean and standard deviation. If we want to insure that the numbers don't go beyond one decimal place, we can imbed formula 6.7 in the round-off function ROUND(num, places):

(6.8) = ROUND(NORM.INV(RAND( ), μ, σ),1)

Note the nesting of parenthesis – each function must be entirely completed ")" inside of its "container function".

There is one word of caution with respect to the use of the RAND() function. Excel will generate a new set of random values –which changes the spreadsheet – every time a new calculation or activity occurs. This can be very disturbing, especially if you have calculated a sample mean and drawn a graph to see how the sample data looks.

One way to compensate for this constant recalculation of random numbers is to take a "snapshot" of the data, that is, copy the column with the RAND.INV command and Paste Special: values only. Then calculate the sample statistics on the new (fixed value) column.

STANDARDIZED SCORES

A normal distribution with $\mu = 0$ and $\sigma = 1$ is called a **standard normal** distribution. Normal distributions with any mean and standard deviation can be converted to standard form, or **z scores** by

$$z = \frac{X - \mu}{\sigma}$$

When calculating z scores in Excel the above formula must be entered using the appropriate cell locations. If you are using SPSS click on the Analyze menu and choose the second option Descriptive Statistics as we did in Chapter 5. In the next list choose Descriptives...

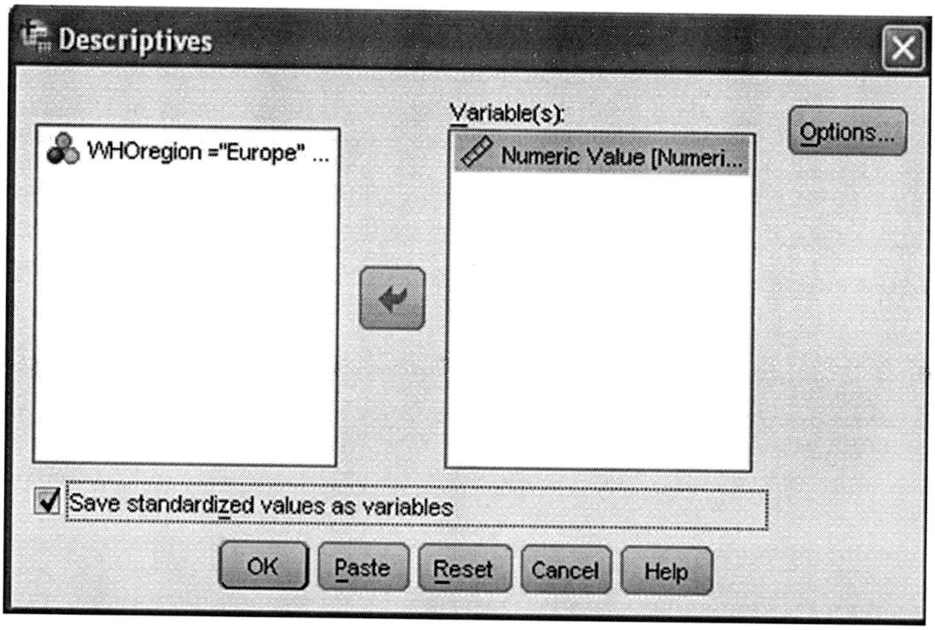

Figure 6.14

Move the data item whose scores you want into the variable list and check the box "Save standardized values as variables" (note that z is underlined indicating z scores.) Click on OK. The z scores will be added to the data view as the last column. There will be a generic title like ZNumeric Value. You can change the title in the variable view which is recommended if you are calculating more than one set of z scores.

Standardized or z scores can be used to create a common scale for studies of the same characteristic with different means and standard deviations.

For example, suppose your math instructor gives you the option of retaking an exam. You had scored an 81 on the first try. You think you can do better so you retake the test and score an 86. The instructor tells you to choose which score you want to keep with the condition that your score will depend on how everyone else did on the two tests and how many scores are lower than yours (a percentile grade). The instructor gives you the information that both tests are normally distributed: test1 $\sim N(60, 15)$ and test2 $\sim N(80, 5)$. Which score should you keep?

By using z scores you can compare the 2 grades. For test1, $z1 = (81 - 60)/15 = 1.4$. The standard score for test2 $= (86 - 80)/5 = 1.2$. The better score was the first one, 81.

Of course, you could have come to the same conclusion had you calculated the probability (percent) that corresponds to each score: test1: P(X< 81) =NORM.DIST(81,60,15,TRUE) = 0.92 and test2: P(X < 86) =NORM.DIST(86,80,5,TRUE) = 0.88. In test1 you scored in the 92nd percentile while in test 2 your score was in the 88th percentile.

Historically, probabilities for normal distributions were calculated by looking at charts that gave the area under the bell curve for a specific score. The same chart was used throughout the mathematics community and was based on standardized scores so the values would be accurate for every normally distributed random variable. This was a very clever device that has probably lost a great deal of its "punch" since computers and calculators have made it possible to calculate the probabilities using the actual means and standard deviation of any experiment.

EXERCISES

1. Each major blood group (O, A, B, AB) is divided into Rh negative or positive types. Type O– blood is considered the "universal donor" because it can be donated to people of any blood type. Type AB+ blood is considered the "universal recipient" because people with this type can receive any blood type. The distribution of all blood types for Americans is shown in table 6.3(infoplease.com http://www.infoplease.com/ipa/A0877658.html#ixzz2i1NAoxGh)

Blood type	Percent (%) of Americans with this type	Who can receive this type
O+	37	O+, A+, B+, AB+
O–	6	All blood types
A+	34	A+, AB+
A–	6	A+, A–, AB+, AB–
B+	10	B+, AB+
B–	2	B+, B–, AB+, AB–
AB+	4	AB+
AB–	1	AB+, AB–

The college is going to run a blood drive. Assuming that the blood types of the sample of volunteers that show up follow the above distribution, answer the following:

a. If a volunteer is selected at random, what is the probability of getting someone with type A– blood?

b. What is the probability of choosing someone who is Rh–?

c. What is the probability of choosing someone who can *receive* AB– blood?

d. If 150 volunteers give blood, how many units of O– would you expect to collect?

e. The first 3 volunteers have agreed to let their blood sample be used in a special study. Let X be a random variable for the number of these volunteers who are Rh–.

- Draw the tree diagram and sample space of the + and – Rh factors of the 3 volunteers.
- Construct the probability distribution for the number of the 3 volunteers who are Rh–.

- Graph the distribution.
- How many of the volunteers do you predict will be Rh–?

2. A particular drug therapy is known to have a 70% cure rate. For a drug trial consisting of 40 patients construct the binomial distribution and the cumulative binomial distribution. Graph both distributions.

   Find the probability that:

   a. 20 people are cured.
   b. more than 30 people are cured.
   c. between 17 and 25 people (inclusive) are cured.
   d. fewer than 10 people are cured.
   e. How many people do you expect to be cured?

3. Suppose the number of patients coming into a hospital emergency room in one hour has a Poisson distribution with parameter $\lambda = 5$. Create the chart for the distribution and the cumulative distribution. Experiment to see how many scores you need to include. Draw the 2 graphs. Use the charts to determine the following probabilities for the arrival of:

   a. exactly 2 patients in one hour.
   b. fewer than 4 patients in one hour.
   c. at least 1 patient in one hour.
   d. at most 6 patients in one hour.

4. Suppose that the weight of college men playing the position of Safety in NCAA Division 1 AA football is normally distributed with a mean of 195 and a standard deviation of 8.

   Graph the associated normal curve and generate the cumulative probability function. Use the curve and chart to determine the probability that a randomly selected safety would weigh:

   a. between 190 and 205 lbs.
   b. more than 215 lbs.
   c. less than 175 lbs.
   d. approximately 210 lbs.

5. Using the distribution of weights of football safeties conjectured in problem 4, N(195,8), simulate a sample of 50 such players.

   a. Find the summary statistics for your sample: mean, median, mode, standard deviation, minimum, maximum and range.
   b. Create the frequency table and histogram for the sample.

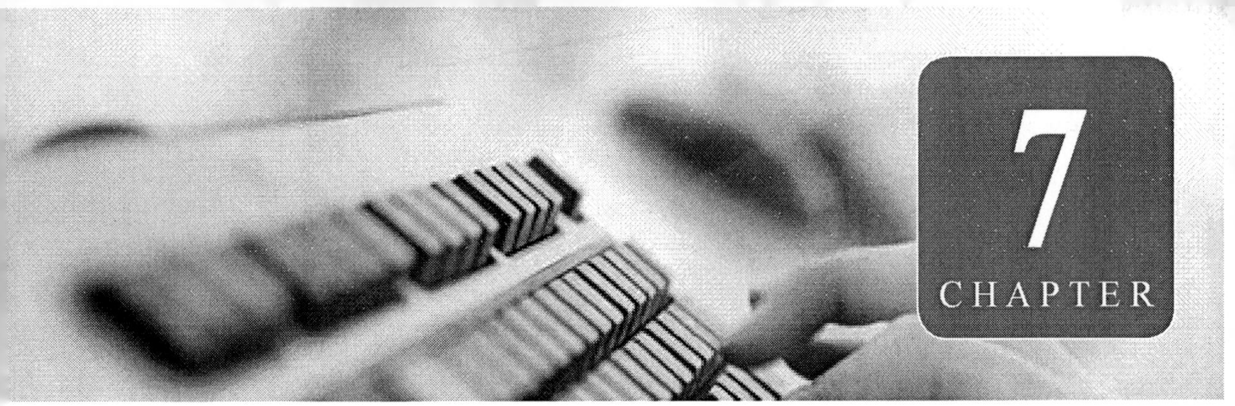

Matrices

We have seen that large collections of data are readily organized in tables, consisting of rows and columns. In mathematics such tables containing numerical or algebraic values are called matrices or in the singular, a matrix. A matrix can also be used as a type of shorthand representation of a system of equations. In the biological sciences, for example, matrices can be used to track population growth (Leslie Matrix).

In this last chapter we will explore some quick manipulations of matrices: their arrangement and their arithmetic. First we will need some basic concepts and terminology:

Size of a matrix: m X n ("m by n"), that is, m rows with n columns

Square matrix: a matrix with size n X n

Notation: matrices may be written with rows and columns inside of square brackets or named with (usually) bold capital letters $\mathbf{A}=\begin{bmatrix} 1 & 3 \\ 2 & 6 \\ 7 & 9 \end{bmatrix}$

Transpose: swapping columns with rows ("flip") m X n → n X m

There are two methods to create the transpose of a matrix. The first is just a copy/paste process. The second uses the TRANSPOSE( )command (see table 7.1 below).

For the first method, copy the cells of the original matrix. Select the starting upper left cell for the Transpose, cell E2 in the example below. Use the Paste Special feature and check off the Transpose box. Paste Special is under the Paste option of the Clipboard group in the Home tab Ribbon in Excel and is located under the Edit menu in Open Office.

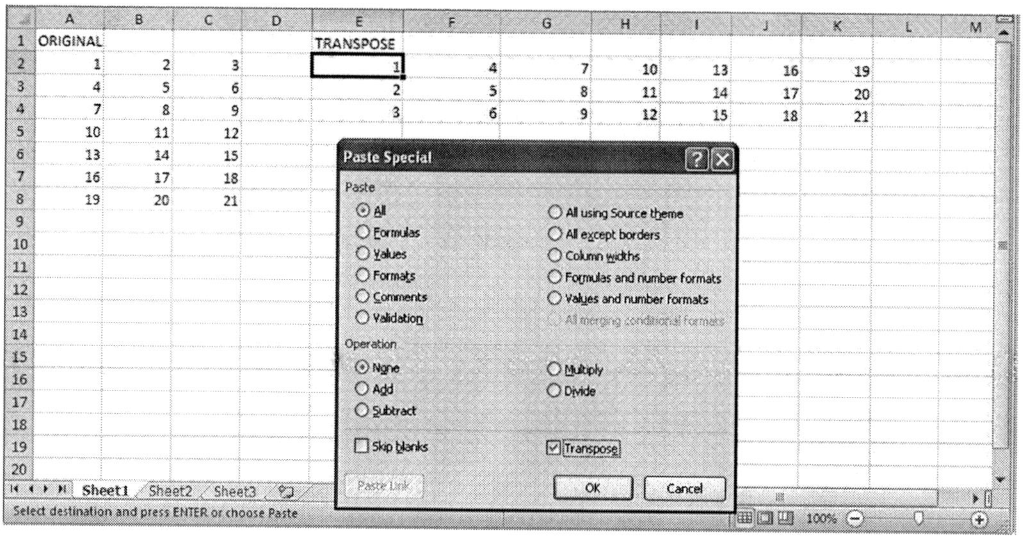

Figure 7.1

Identity Matrix: the n X n matrix with 1's along the main diagonal and zeroes everywhere else is called the identity matrix. The 3 X 3 Identity Matrix is

$$I=\begin{bmatrix}1 & 0 & 0\\ 0 & 1 & 0\\ 0 & 0 & 1\end{bmatrix}$$ and has the special property that $\mathbf{I}\cdot\mathbf{A}=\mathbf{A}\cdot\mathbf{I}=\mathbf{A}$

A Matrix can be **named** in the spreadsheet:

First select the m X n matrix. Then use the Formulas Tab, Defined Names Group, Define Name

(OpenOffice: Insert Menu/ Names/ Define...)

Choose the option to specify the name of the matrix. You can then use that name in formulas such as **A+B.**

In order to remove or edit a named object, use the Name Manager in the Defined Names group of the Formulas tab.

ARITHMETIC

Matrix functions are typically array functions so it is important to keep in mind a critical rule in manipulating matrices: **Size Matters!** You need to reserve the correct amount of space for the answer and you need to make sure that the matrices have the correct size for the operation to be legal.

Below is a summary of key matrix operations with the required sizes of the matrices and the size of the resulting matrix for each operation. All of the following are executed as array functions. Note that the TRANSPOSE command can be used in calculations while the copy/paste special discussed above cannot.

Operation	Comment	Size	Size Of Result
Addition	Matrices must be the same size	m X n + m X n	m X n
Subtraction	Matrices must be the same size	m X n – m X n	m X n
Multiplication (MMULT)	The number of rows in the first matrix = number of columns in the second matrix. NOTE: Matrix multiplication IS NOT COMMUTATIVE!	m X n ·n X r	m X r
Inverse (MINVERSE) A^{-1}	Square matrices only* Note: $AA^{-1} = A^{-1}A = I$	n X n	n X n
Determinant (MDETERM) det(A) or $\lvert A \rvert$	Square matrices only*	n X n	Single value
Transpose (TRANSPOSE) A^T	All matrices	m X n	n X m

Table 7.1

*A square matrix may not have an inverse. If the determinant (a single number associated with the elements of the matrix) = 0, the matrix has no inverse and is said to be *singular.* A matrix which has an inverse is called *nonsingular.*

If you have named the matrices, then to add or subtract you need only highlight the target cells that will store the sum or difference, type the formula = A + B, for example, and press **[Shift + Ctrl + Enter]** to execute the array function command. (See beginning of Chapter 5)

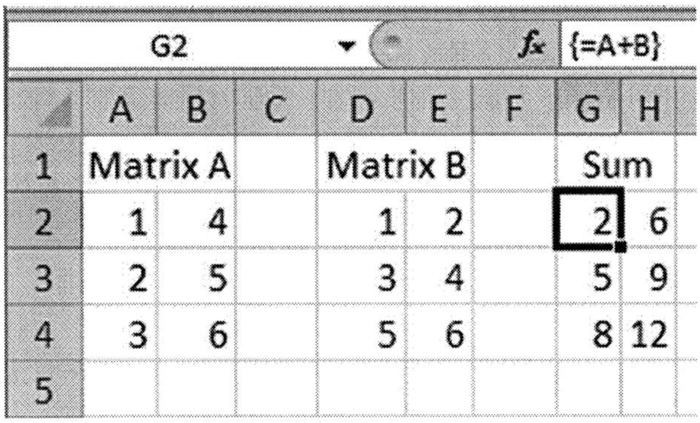

Figure 7.2

If the matrices are not named, then highlight the range of cells for each matrix. The formula bar will show = A2:B4+D2:E4. As usual, the curly braces { } will be added when you press **[Shift + Ctrl + Enter]**.

The following is an example of matrix multiplication for the product **AC**. A range of cells has been used to identify each matrix.

K2 — fx {=MMULT(A2:B4,G2:I3)}

	A	B	C	D	E	F	G	H	I	J	K	L	M
1	Matrix A			Matrix B			Matrix C				Product AC		
2	1	4		1	2		0	2	4		24	34	44
3	2	5		3	4		6	8	10		30	44	58
4	3	6		5	6						36	54	72
5													

Figure 7.3

Note that **A** is a 3 X 2 matrix and **C** is 2 X 3 resulting in a 3 X 3 product. While the product **AB** does not exist, we can find the product of **A** and TRANSPOSE(**B**) written mathematically as $\mathbf{AB}^T$.

K2 — fx {=MMULT(A,TRANSPOSE(B))}

	A	B	C	D	E	F	G	H	I	J	K	L	M
1	Matrix A			Matrix B			Matrix C				Product AB^T		
2	1	4		1	2		0	2	4		9	19	29
3	2	5		3	4		6	8	10		12	26	40
4	3	6		5	6						15	33	51
5													

Figure 7.4

SOLVING A SYSTEM OF EQUATIONS

Consider a simple linear equation:

$$2x = 4$$

We can **solve** this equation, that is, find the value of x that makes the statement true, by multiplying each side of the equation by the multiplicative inverse of 2, the coefficient of x.

$$\tfrac{1}{2} \cdot 2x = \tfrac{1}{2} \cdot 4 \text{ or } x = 2.$$

When we have a system of n equations with n variables, we can create a matrix of the coefficients, find the inverse of the matrix and if it exists, use it to solve for the variables as shown below.

The system can be written as **Ax = b**

where **A** is the n X n matrix of coefficients, and **x** and **b** are each n X 1 matrices (also called vectors) representing the variables on the left and the constants on the right-hand side of the equations.

So, multiplying each side of the equation on the left by $\mathbf{A}^{-1}$ we have:

$$\mathbf{A}^{-1}\mathbf{A}\mathbf{x} = \mathbf{A}^{-1}\mathbf{b}$$

$$\mathbf{I}\mathbf{x} = \mathbf{A}^{-1}\mathbf{b}$$

$$\mathbf{x} = \mathbf{A}^{-1}\mathbf{b} \tag{7.1}$$

Suppose we wish to solve the system

$$2x + 3y = 6$$

$$-2x + 3y = 10$$

We can write the system in matrix notation as

$$\begin{bmatrix} 2 & 3 \\ -2 & 3 \end{bmatrix} \cdot \begin{bmatrix} x \\ y \end{bmatrix} = \begin{bmatrix} 6 \\ 10 \end{bmatrix}$$

Where **A** is the coefficient matrix $\begin{bmatrix} 2 & 3 \\ -2 & 3 \end{bmatrix}$ and **b** is the vector of constants on the right hand side $\begin{bmatrix} 6 \\ 10 \end{bmatrix}$. We can find the value of the variable vector **x** shown above as $\begin{bmatrix} x \\ y \end{bmatrix}$ by using the inverse function, highlighting cells E2:F3, and typing =MINVERSE(A2:B3), **[Shift + Ctrl + Enter].**

A fraction cell format has been used for a more intuitive presentation of the inverse.

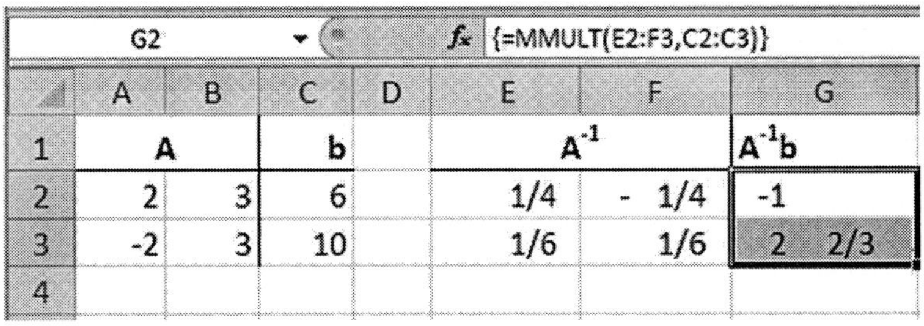

G2 fx {=MMULT(E2:F3,C2:C3)}

	A	B	C	D	E	F	G
1	A		b		A^{-1}		$A^{-1}b$
2	2	3	6		1/4	- 1/4	-1
3	-2	3	10		1/6	1/6	2 2/3
4							

Figure 7.5

Calculate $\mathbf{A}^{-1}\mathbf{b}$ using the array function MMULT: =MMULT(E2:F3,C2:C3), **[Shift + Ctrl + Enter].** Remember to highlight the column G2:G3 before you begin the command. The solution to the system is x= -1 and y = 2.67.

If we convert the two equations to the form y= mx+b, we can graph the system and its solution.

Equation 1 is rewritten as y= -2/3 x+2 and equation 2 as y = 2/3 x + 10/3.

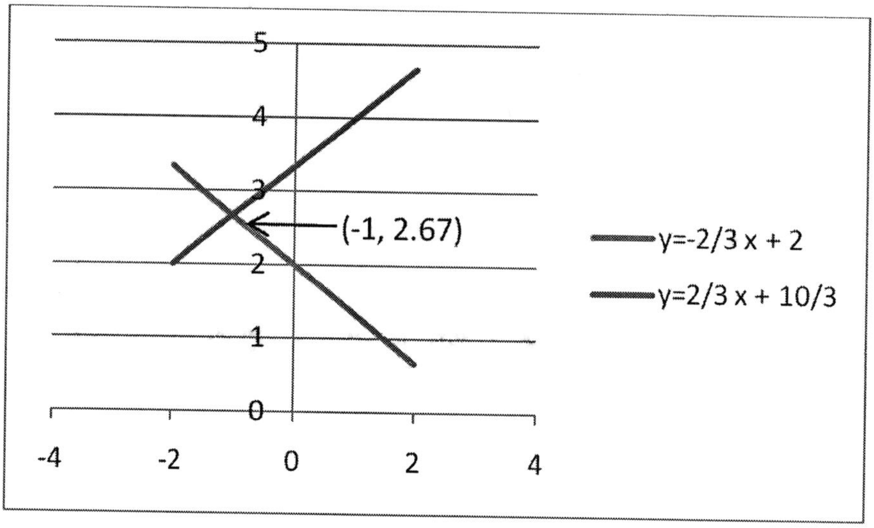

Figure 7.6

Of course for a system with only 2 equations and 2 unknowns this might not seem worth the effort, but same amount of work can solve very large systems as long as $\mathbf{A}^{-1}$ exists.

EXERCISES:

1. Using the Matrices **A, B** and **C** in figure 7.3, calculate
   a. **CA**
   b. $\mathbf{BA}^T$
2. For the following set of equations:

   10x + 12y + 15z = 40

   11x + 12y + 14z = 80

   3x + 4y + 4z = 24

   a. formulate the appropriate matrix for the system **AX= b.**
   b. solve the system by means of $\mathbf{X} = \mathbf{A}^{-1}\mathbf{b}$.
   c. clearly state the solution.
   d. Check your results by showing that your answer satisfies the system **AX= b**

$-2 \cdot 2 + 1 \cdot 4$

$-4 + 4$

10x + 12y + 15z = 40
11x + 12y + 14z = 80
3x + 4y + 4z = 24

$$\begin{bmatrix} 10 & 12 & 15 \\ 11 & 12 & 14 \\ 3 & 4 & 4 \end{bmatrix} \begin{bmatrix} 40 \\ 80 \\ 24 \end{bmatrix}$$

References

Exercises Chapter 2 #1 and 5 #1:

"Procedures to Determine the Amount of Plant Cover in Field Plots", Lance S. Evans, Sr. Joan Harnett and Zella Kahn-Jetter, Environmental and Experimental Botany (EEB), Vol. 58, Issues 1-3, December 2006, Pages 180-187.

SOME DATA RESOURCES:

1. The Math Forum @ Drexel (http://mathforum.org/library/topics/data_sets/)
2. The Quantitative Environmental Learning Project (QELP), Greg Langkamp and Joe Hull, Seattle Central Community College, (http://www.seattlecentral.edu/qelp/sets/001/001.html)
3. World Health Organization (www.who.int/research/en).
4. ClinicalTrials.gov

Olympics Data:

5. www.databaseOlympics.com
6. www.olympic.org

Government Sites:

7. http://healthdata.gov
8. www.census.gov
9. The Center for Disease Control (http://www.cdc.gov/nchs/hdi.htm)